LIFE NATURE LIBRARY

THE UNIVERSE

OTHER BOOKS BY THE EDITORS OF LIFE:

LIFE'S PICTURE HISTORY OF WORLD WAR II

LIFE'S PICTURE HISTORY OF WESTERN MAN

THE WORLD WE LIVE IN
  with Lincoln Barnett

THE WORLD'S GREAT RELIGIONS

AMERICA'S ARTS AND SKILLS

PICTURE COOK BOOK

THE SECOND WORLD WAR
  with Winston S. Churchill

THE WONDERS OF LIFE ON EARTH
  with Lincoln Barnett

LIFE WORLD LIBRARY

LIFE PICTORIAL ATLAS OF THE WORLD
  with The Editors of Rand McNally

THE EPIC OF MAN

THE LIFE TREASURY OF AMERICAN FOLKLORE

LIFE GUIDE TO PARIS

LIFE NATURE LIBRARY

THE UNIVERSE

by David Bergamini
and The Editors of LIFE

TIME INCORPORATED
NEW YORK

A
STONEHENGE
BOOK

About the Author

David Bergamini is the son of a missionary architect whose work took him and his family to many places in the Far East. Bergamini was born in Tokyo, spent his childhood in China and was a 13-year-old living in the Philippines when World War II broke out. He was put in a concentration camp and spent much of his time studying mathematics, which led to an interest in astronomy. After the war he went to Dartmouth, majoring in English and minoring in mathematics, and was a Rhodes scholar at Oxford from 1949 to 1951. He spent 10 years with LIFE Magazine as a reporter and editor in the science department before leaving to devote his full time to writing. While with LIFE, he was one of the staff that produced *The World We Live In*. He has had a number of articles published on scientific subjects, including "The Language of Science," which has been reprinted in essay anthologies. He is also the author of *The Fleet in the Window*, a novel drawn from his wartime experiences in a Philippine prison camp.

On the Cover

A distant nebula, its gases glowing bright from the radiation of a hidden star buried in its depths, looks red because it is in back of a dust cloud which blots out other colors which are present in the spectrum of light.

Contents

TIME INC. BOOK DIVISION

Editor: NORMAN P. ROSS

Copy Director: WILLIAM JAY GOLD   *Art Director:* EDWARD A. HAMILTON

Chief of Research: BEATRICE T. DOBIE

EDITORIAL STAFF FOR "THE UNIVERSE"

Editor, LIFE Nature Library: MAITLAND A. EDEY

Assistants to the Editor: GEORGE McCUE, JOHN PAUL PORTER

Copy Editor: JOHN PURCELL

Designer: PAUL JENSEN

Chief Researcher: MARTHA TURNER

Researchers: DORIS BRY, PEGGY BUSHONG, ELEANOR FELTSER, LE CLAIR G. LAMBERT,
PAULA NORWORTH, ROXANNA SAYRE, PAUL W. SCHWARTZ, VICTOR H. WALDROP,
ROGER B. WIESENBACH, PHYLLIS M. WILLIAMSON

Picture Researchers: MARGARET K. GOLDSMITH, JOAN T. LYNCH

Art Associate: ROBERT L. YOUNG

Art Assistants: JAMES D. SMITH, MARK A. BINN

Copy Staff: MARIAN GORDON GOLDMAN, SUZANNE SEIXAS, DOLORES A. LITTLES

Publisher: JEROME S. HARDY

General Manager: JOHN WATTERS

LIFE MAGAZINE

| *Editor* | *Managing Editor* | *Publisher* |
| EDWARD K. THOMPSON | GEORGE P. HUNT | C. D. JACKSON |

The text for the chapters of this book was written by David Bergamini, for the picture essays by Harvey B. Loomis, Percy Knauth, Robert McClung, Peter Meyerson, David Bergamini, John Purcell and John Stanton. The following individuals and departments of LIFE Magazine were especially helpful in the production of the book: Fritz Goro, Dmitri Kessel, Margaret Bourke-White, Larry Burrows and Ralph Morse, staff photographers, and Doris O'Neil, Chief of the LIFE Picture Library. Valuable assistance was also given by Donald Bermingham of the TIME-LIFE News Service, and Content Peckham, Chief of the Time Inc. Bureau of Editorial Reference.

Introduction

THE advances in photography during the past century have been a boon to inquisitive mankind. More than that, they have transformed many of the sciences and arts. If astronomers were still dependent on the human eye for their knowledge of the universe, relatively slim would that knowledge be, even though telescopic lenses and mirrors supplementing the eye were doing their frantic best to reach distant galaxies and unravel cosmic chemistry. Indeed, without photography this elegant pictorial treatment of the universe would not have been possible.

We pause to wonder wistfully if there may not be some yet unknown tool for prying into the microcosm and the macrocosm that will, when developed, break through our barriers of ignorance as sensationally as the photographic processes removed much of our blindness of a century ago. Can it be that the radio telescopes, which do not use photography, and the photoelectron tubes are such implements? There are so many unknowns, and still more unknowables—unknowable to our present mental and sense-organ equipment. Where should we look for a break-through—in the psychology of animals, in the realm of a completely new mathematics, in the science of personality, in subelectronics, in the fruitful elimination of superstition and the irrational?

A wonderful prospect lies ahead for those who tackle the universe; but how pitiably weak it would be if it were not for the photochemical processes which have so greatly aided and guided the researches and permitted as well this absorbing story about them.

Some photographs record a million of the stars of our galaxy. Others, groping for the bounds of the universe, uncover thousands of other galaxies. Ten times as many galaxies inhabit our explorable space-time as there are men on this crowded planet. There are indeed galaxies enough for everybody!

HARLOW SHAPLEY
Harvard University

AN UNRESOLVED MYSTERY lurks in a dark, jutting cloud of opaque gas obscuring part of Monoceros, a constellation 4,000 light-years away. Man may never know how the gas cloud got there, or what is behind it.

1

Myths
and Misconceptions

WE of the latter 20th Century are living on the eve of man's supreme adventure: his first tentative flights away from the earth that gave him birth toward the unmeasured expanses of the universe. Before this ultimate quest of the human spirit can be completed, the stars may well burn out and life and the universe itself fade away. But that will be billions of years from now, if ever. In our own time, the little steps will be taken: men will climb the mountains of the moon, penetrate the mists of Venus, stride the rusty deserts of Mars. Within centuries, whole colonies may embark on voyages that will last for generations. Within thousands of years, the children of the planet earth may be scattered among the stars, separated far more irrevocably from their fellows at home than ever Virginians were from Englishmen or the Polynesians from mainland Asia in the great migrations of the past.

Ironically, this age of human daring and resourcefulness is dawning at a time when man's concept of the larger cosmos beyond his own planet is more humbling than ever before. Whereas he once thought with utmost confidence that the entire universe—moon, sun, planets and myriad stars—revolved around him, he now knows that the earth is one smallish planet of a medium-sized star in the outskirts of only one among uncounted billions of galaxies. Man has not yet begun to amass knowledge even of the nearby moon at firsthand, but he has penetrated many of the greatest mysteries of space by observing celestial events at a distance and making careful deductions about what he has seen. Well-traveled astronauts of the future, reminiscing over the sunsets or moonscapes of other planets, will seem incomparably sophisticated. Yet the not-so-dashing, earthbound astronomers of here and now have already glimpsed the over-all vistas and overwhelming perspectives of the universe. Tracing its outlines has been an enthralling adventure for the bold minds which have carried out the task.

From earliest prehistory, man has gazed into the flat confusion of the night sky and pondered the glittering configurations he saw there. Before writing was invented, man had names for the celestial bodies. Before he conceived of ethical systems, he bowed to images of the sun and moon. Before he devised sandglasses or water clocks, he followed the heavenly motions, numbering the days, months, seasons and years. To nomad and seafarer, the stars in the sky were signposts that told direction. To farmer and herdsman, the moon's phases and the sun's annual journey foretold the times of planting and of rains. The earliest astronomy was an eminently practical pursuit long before the cause in which it was undertaken earned the name of a science. Out of the endeavor many sciences were born—Pythagorean geometry, Newtonian dynamics, Einsteinian physics and cosmology.

MAPS OF THE STARS

The maps on these pages show the brighter constellations visible in the Northern and Southern Hemispheres. The constellations are named in capital letters; the stars in lower-case letters with a capital initial. The Big Dipper, one of the most prominent features of the northern skies, is actually a part of the larger constellation Ursa Major. The Milky Way is seen as a cloudy blue belt across each map.

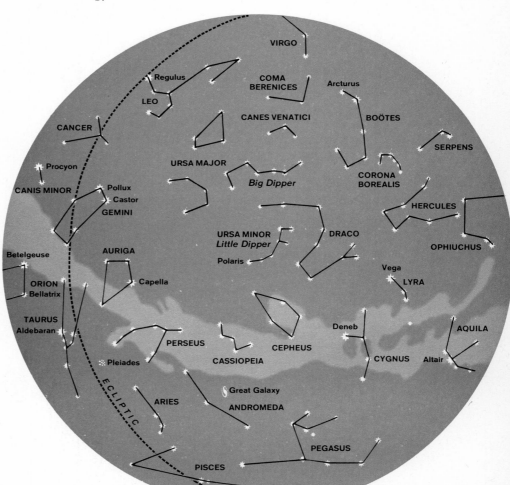

Man's path to the launching pad has not been easy. Many ideas that seem common sense today were once the very opposite. They contradicted what the eye saw and required pyramids of difficult deductions and endless nights of watching with crude instruments before they could be proved. The sky, in the eyes of the first observers, was a great vault, set nightly with tiny flecks of fire. The sun moved across the vault every day, rising out of the seas to the east and plunging to bed in the western ocean. The pale moon, brightest of all bodies in the night sky, seemed to be some sort of feminine creature, waxing and waning on a 29-day cycle.

But even this simple picture of the heavens contained difficulties. A person armed with nothing but a straight stick could see that the sun's daily path across the sky was not changeless. Moreover, the wheel of its seasons brought heat and cold, floods and drought. A count of the moon's recurrent extinctions helped to time these seasonal changes approximately, but not exactly: by moon-count, the floods of spring or the rains of autumn might come early or late. It took the patient counting of untold generations to discover that 12 lunar months do not make exactly a year, but fall 11 days short. And what could be said about eclipses, when the bright master of day or the softer lamp of the night was slowly extinguished, only to be restored?

More puzzling still, the fiery flecks of the stars were all sensibly fixed in place on the revolving, heavenly vault; all, that is, except for five erratic wanderers,

THE BRIGHTEST STARS

Of the 7,000 stars visible to an unaided eye on earth, the 25 which look the brightest are listed below in the order of their apparent brilliance. This is not the same as true brilliance. Deneb, for example, is actually the brightest of the 25, but ranks only 19th because it is so far away.

NAME	TRUE BRIGHTNESS (SUN 1)	DISTANCE (LIGHT-YEARS)
Alpha Canis Majoris (Sirius)	23	8.7
Alpha Carinae (Canopus)	1,500	100
Alpha Centauri	1.5	4.3
Alpha Boötis (Arcturus)	110	36
Alpha Lyrae (Vega)	55	27
Alpha Aurigae (Capella)	170	47
Beta Orionis (Rigel)	40,000	800
Alpha Canis Minoris (Procyon)	7.3	11.3
Alpha Orionis (Betelgeuse)	17,000	500
Alpha Eridani (Achernar)	200	65
Beta Centauri	5,000	300
Alpha Aquilae (Altair)	11	16.5
Alpha Crucis	4,000	400
Alpha Tauri (Aldebaran)	100	53
Alpha Virginis (Spica)	2,800	260
Alpha Scorpii (Antares)	5,000	400
Beta Geminorum (Pollux)	45	40
Alpha Piscis Australis (Fomalhaut)	14	23
Alpha Cygni (Deneb)	60,000	1,400
Beta Crucis	6,000	500
Alpha Leonis (Regulus)	120	75
Epsilon Canis Majoris (Adhara)	8,000	600
Lambda Scorpii (Shaula)	1,700	300
Alpha Geminorum (Castor)	27	45
Gamma Orionis (Bellatrix)	2,300	360

Note: When the star is one of a double or multiple system, the brightness printed in the table is that of the principal component.

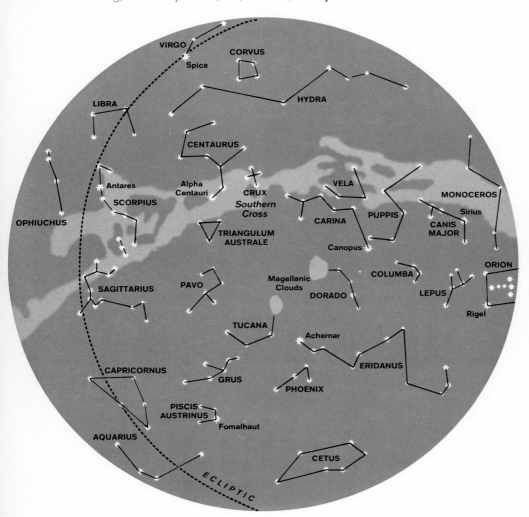

Archimedes (287-212 B.C.), Greek-born mathematician and astronomer, lived in Syracuse. He formulated laws governing gears, pulleys and levers, discovered the principle of liquid displacement and was the first to master astronomical numbers.

the visible planets that we know as Mercury, Venus, Mars, Jupiter and Saturn. Sometimes, too, even the sober fraternity of fixed stars was increased by what seemed to be an entirely new member— a nova, or supernova as it is called now —that blazed up out of darkness, remained bright enough even for daytime notice during a few weeks or months, and then once more subsided into obscurity.

With the rise of civilization, some men could devote their lives to a study of these and other celestial mysteries. In ancient Mesopotamia, the priests kept such detailed, statistical records of the motions of sun, moon and planets that they could roughly predict lunar eclipses without understanding what caused them. They mapped the yearly path—the plane of the ecliptic, as it is called— of the sun across the heavens. They accurately counted the time between full moons as a little over 29½ days. They also built seven-story towers—probably in honor of the sun, moon and five planets—which the captive Hebrews, in their antagonism toward such worship, immortalized as the Tower of Babel.

Of all the ancient civilizations of the Old World, only that of the Chinese— who recorded eclipses as far back as 4000 B.C. and built numerous observatories —came close to rivaling the Mesopotamians' in accurate observations. In the New World, however, the Mayas were superlative astronomers. Their calendar was, in many ways, more convenient than the system of weeks, months, years and February 29ths we use today. They predicted eclipses and worked out the length of the solar year and the lunar month with amazing precision. Unfortunately, since we can read only the Mayas' numbers and not their words, the full extent of their astronomical knowledge remains unknown.

IN all early civilizations, what we call astronomy went hand in glove with astrology, superstition and primitive priestly religion. The first truly scientific astronomers appeared among the Greeks. The Greeks had an invaluable scientific asset—geometry—which they developed, along with astronomy, into a marvelous intellectual instrument. The first—and conceptually the best—school of Greek astronomy grew up not in Greece itself but in the Greek cities south of Troy along the present Turkish coast. In the city of Miletus, as early as 600 B.C., the philosopher Thales conceived of the earth as round. Two centuries later, the disciples of Pythagoras maintained that the earth was spherical and also moved through space. Unfortunately, the Pythagoreans mixed their brilliant deductions with mystic numerology. They had evidence for nine different circular motions in the sky: that of the fixed stars and those of the five planets, the earth, moon and sun. But nine, in their view, was an "imperfect" number, so they brought the total up to 10 by inventing an "anti-earth" that always stayed on the far side of the world where it could never be seen—at least not by Greeks.

The views of Plato (427-347 B.C.) on astronomy typified both the confusion and the open-mindedness of the times. At the beginning of his philosophic career, he imagined that the gods drove shining chariots across the sky. Later, he wondered whether the earth was flat or round. He decided on roundness—the shape of the earth's shadow on the moon during a lunar eclipse was strong evidence—but at first he kept the earth unmoving at the center of things. Then he was shown that earthly rotation on an axis—and possibly revolution in an orbit as well—best fitted the evidence. Finally, as an old man, he "was very sorry," reports the historian Plutarch, "that he had located the earth in the center of the universe, in a place not fitting for it . . . since the central and most noble place should be reserved for something more worthy."

After the conquests of Alexander the Great, when the cultural capital of

Ptolemy (lived circa A.D. 140), a Greco-Egyptian astronomer, first systematized the theory that the universe was revolving around a stationary earth at its center. The doctrine, found in the Almagest, was accepted through the entire Middle Ages.

Greece moved from Athens to Alexandria in Egypt, the earth-moving school of astronomy continued to put forward brilliantly correct theories. Aristarchus of Samos (310-230 B.C.) maintained with so much conviction that the earth rotates, revolves and is not the center of the cosmos that he was severely censured for impiety. Seleucus observed that the tides are connected with the phases of the moon. Eratosthenes compared noon sightings of the sun at the summer solstice from points 500 miles apart and calculated the earth's circumference. For most Greeks, however, the idea of being "Roll'd round in earth's diurnal course, With rocks, and stones, and trees," as Wordsworth put it, remained preposterous and heretical. The imaginative Greeks who glimpsed the true nature of the solar system failed to back their ideas with a coherent mathematical explanation which would account for the observations of the best astronomers.

CONSERVATIVE workaday stargazers gradually adopted a more consistent although more complicated representation of the motions they saw in the sky. Their theory was finally formulated by one of the most careful and scientific of all Greek astronomers, Hipparchus, who worked in Rhodes and Alexandria about 150 B.C. According to Hipparchus' observations and calculations, the spherical earth was stationary; the sun, moon and planets circled round the earth in a major sweep; and at the same time these bodies pursued other circular courses centered on the first.

Today it seems absurd that a monstrous mass of stone like a planet should focus all its motions around a point in empty space, but before the idea of gravity it seemed as reasonable as any other assumption. And the virtue of Hipparchus' complicated geometry was that it accurately represented the motions that the early astronomers observed and made predictions possible. Such mysteries as retrograde motion—when a planet seems to slow down, stand still and then double back on itself in the sky—could all be predicted geometrically by Hipparchus' system of circles, or "epicycles and deferents" as they were called. His system was perfected about A.D. 140 by Claudius Ptolemy and handed down through the Middle Ages in the form of an astronomical encyclopedia—Ptolemy's famous Almagest. This system was so good that it withstood the tests of observation for another 13 centuries. Because of Ptolemy's work, Hipparchus' scheme became known to the Moslem world—and later to the Europeans—as the Ptolemaic system.

Great technical difficulties put blinders on the vision of the Greeks and helped the Ptolemaic system to go unchallenged during the dark centuries of classical decline and barbarian unconcern. The two largest of these difficulties were time and number. Time was a problem because there was no really precise way of measuring it. What use, after all, were accurate fixes on planet positions at midnight without sure knowledge that it really was midnight? Number was a problem because the ancients had no good way of expressing it. In the notation used by the Romans and Alexandrian Greeks, the smallest astronomic quantities seemed almost inexpressible. In Roman numerals, for instance, the mileage to the moon would have had to be written CCXXXMMMMMMMMDCCCLVII instead of 238,857. Today, this difficulty may seem no more than a minor matter of clumsy notation, but to the ancients it was a major mental block. Only Archimedes of Syracuse (287-212 B.C.), one of the last of the great Greek scientists, was ever completely at home with big numbers. Some idea of his towering inventiveness can be gleaned from the fact that he formulated most of the mathematical laws governing levers, pulleys, gears and hydraulics—that is,

Nicholas Copernicus (1473-1543), a Polish astronomer, revolutionized the worlds of science, religion and culture by proving that the sun is at the center of our solar system, and that the earth, along with the other planets, is revolving around it.

Johannes Kepler (1571-1630), a German astronomer, was influenced by the teachings of Copernicus. He discovered that planetary orbits are elliptical; that planets speed up when they are close to the sun, and slow down when far away from it.

much of everyday mechanics. He is also credited with having held a Roman armada at bay for three years with engines of war that hurled huge boulders at the enemy ships or lifted them bodily out of the water to smash them against the Sicilian cliffs. The opposing Roman general Marcellus called him "this geometrical Briareus who uses our ships like cups to ladle water from the sea."

Where big numbers were concerned, Archimedes saw such difficulty that he devoted a whole treatise to the subject, which he entitled *The Sand Reckoner.* "There are some," he wrote, "who think that the number of the sand is infinite in multitude. . . . Again there are some who, without regarding it as infinite, yet think that no number has been named which is great enough to exceed its multitude. . . . But I will try to show . . . that, of the numbers named by me . . . some exceed not only the number of the mass of sand equal in magnitude to the earth filled up . . . but also that of a mass equal in magnitude to the universe." The largest unit that the Greeks used was a myriad—10,000. Archimedes showed, by a series of virtuoso calculations with cumbersome numerals, that his fancied universe could hold less than the following number of sand grains: a myriad of myriads multiplied by itself seven times and then multiplied by a thousand myriads. Today, mathematicians represent this huge number as the numeral 1 followed by 63 zeros (or as 10^{63}).

Numbers like 10^{63} are still big enough to deal with the universe we know today. The world's largest telescope, for instance, sees out to the edge of a volume of about 10^{67} cubic miles (1 followed by 67 zeros). The number of electrons that could be packed into a sphere as big as the earth is about 10^{63}. In visualizing very big or small things alike, modern man deals with Archimedean-sized numbers. And though he can now express them easily, he cannot truly appreciate their magnitude without reperforming some of Archimedes' mental acrobatics.

THE principal service that the Middle Ages performed for astronomy was to provide time for the development of clocks and for the acceptance of Arabic numeration. Actually, Arabic numerals were not perfected in Arabia at all, but in India. There, about A.D. 500, the Hindus started using a 10-number (decimal) notation in which each number's position showed what power of 10 it represented, while the empty positions were designated by zeros. From India the new numeration spread west to the Moslem world and finally, through trading and crusading, it reached the capitals of Christendom about A.D. 1100.

Along with nimbler numbers, the Christian world got from the Arabs its first translations of the astronomical works of pre-Ptolemaic Greeks. It also acquired many Arabic words for things in astronomy: among them zenith, nadir and almanac. Some important instruments, too, were copied from the Moslems but the all-important clock seems to have had its main development in Europe. The first mechanical clocks appeared toward the end of the 13th Century. They were run not by springs but by descending weights that hung from strings, and they were not very accurate. Even in A.D. 1450, the best of the pre-Copernican Italian astronomers, Toscanelli, was seldom able to give anything more exact about his observations than the nearest hour and the date.

By A.D. 1500, the improved quality of astronomical observation was making the ancient Ptolemaic theory creak distressingly to accommodate new facts. The man who threw the final bomb into the celestial machinery was the Polish astronomer Copernicus (1473-1543)—and he did his best to make it look as if he were only oiling the rusty parts. He dethroned the earth and put the sun at the

An ancient water clock, or clepsydra, had the problem of running at different speeds, since day, for the ancients, started at sunrise and ended at sunset—giving the hours different lengths at different seasons of the year. One ingenious device for changing the clock's speed was a small "movable" hole set on a wheel at the side of the upper tank. When the hole was turned to its lowest position, water would run out of the tank more quickly than when it was in its highest position, there then being less pressure behind it. The float in the lower tank would rise at the proper rate, and time could be told by it. The float could also be used to rotate a star map, and the positions of the constellations read through a permanent grid placed in front of them.

center of all the planetary orbits. But he still showed the orbits as circles and, in a number of cases, he used Ptolemaic epicycles. What is more, it was not until the very end of his life, when he was a venerable, decrepit ecclesiastic, that his discovery was published.

All the precautions of Copernicus were to no avail. Martin Luther called him a fool and his theories anti-Biblical and intolerable. The Pope (Paul III) was inclined to be more tolerant, but many bishops and cardinals agreed with Luther. Copernicus' kindred scientific spirits naturally rallied to his defense. One of them was burned at the stake, others saw their careers blighted and their names smirched with the charge of heresy. Copernicanism became such a thorny theological matter that the best observational astronomer of the 16th Century, Tycho Brahe, would have no part of it. But the data Tycho compiled at his elaborate observatories in Denmark—the most accurate ever assembled up to that time— only served to make the Copernican system indisputable.

W HEN Galileo (1564-1642) first turned a telescope on the skies, in 1609, he found the Copernican system staring him in the face. Around the planet Jupiter he saw four moons circling: clear proof that the one-mooned earth could not be the pre-eminent member of celestial society. With his telescope, Galileo could also observe the moonlike phases of Venus. The fact that Venus showed a fully lighted phase when she was near the sun could not be explained by the Ptolemaic system but only by a Copernican scheme which would allow Venus to circle round the far side of the sun. Because of these observations, Galileo became such an ardent Copernican that the Inquisition forced him to recant and placed him—protesting quietly—under permanent house arrest. He was forbidden ever to raise the matter again, and Galileo went on to spend the rest of his days in the study of mechanics and dynamics.

By the next generation, churchly opposition to a sun-centered universe was waning. In the Protestant north, the successor to Tycho Brahe had been Johannes Kepler (1571-1630). Using Tycho's observations, he showed that a planet does not travel in that exactly circular orbit so vital to Greek "perfection," but instead in a slightly elliptical one, with the sun at one focus of the ellipse. This was the first of Kepler's three laws—the three essential laws of the solar system which he had the luck and wit to discover singlehandedly. The second law is that the planets, in their ellipses, move faster when close to the sun than they do in the more remote parts of their orbits. The third is that the varying times they take in the course of orbiting are proportional when squared, to their distances from the sun, when cubed.

Kepler's three laws, together with Galileo's pioneering work on mechanics, formed the basis for Isaac Newton's universal law of gravitation. Newton (1642-1727) was 22 when he discovered it. "I deduced," he wrote later, "that the forces which keep the planets in their orbs must be reciprocally as the squares of their distances from the centers about which they revolve." It was another 22 years before Newton published his theories in his book, the *Principia*. But then everything fell into place. The forces acting on the planets as they circled the sun were two. The first, centrifugal force, was a matter of inertia, making the planets try to fly off on straight lines into space like balls whirled on a string that suddenly breaks. The second force was gravity, an unbreakable string, that made the planets find their orbits at a distance from the sun where their centrifugal forces exactly balanced the sun's gravitational attraction.

Newton saw that not only the sun but every other object exerts gravity

ROMAN NUMERALS

Unwieldy numerals used by the Romans made simple multiplication and division difficult, not so much because of the mathematics involved, but because of the great amount of space the numerals occupied, as is illustrated in the example below.

XXVI (26)
XII (12)

The Romans multiplied each numeral in XXVI (26) by each numeral in XII (12) as follows:

X times XXVI:
X times X = XXXXXXXXXX or C (100)
X times X = XXXXXXXXXX or C (100)
X times V = VVVVVVVVVV or L (50)
X times I = IIIIIIIIII or X (10)

I times XXVI :
I times X = X (10)
I times X = X (10)
I times V = V (5)
I times I = I (1)

I times XXVI :
I times X = X (10)
I times X = X (10)
I times V = V (5)
I times I = I (1)

total: CC L XXXXX VV II
or
CCC X II which equals 312

according to the amount of matter it contains (its mass). He saw that what makes terrestrial objects fall is the gravitational power of the earth's mass. He was able to calculate the pull of the earth's mass on the moon and so explain why the moon moves as fast and as far out as it does. He explained that the mass of the moon, pulling in its turn, sucks up the earth's surface fluids into the tides of the ocean. The masses of the planets, the shape of the earth (flattened at the poles), even the trajectories of cannon balls all submitted peacefully to the mathematics engendered by Newton's central idea about gravity.

After Newton's death, his ideas and equations triumphantly swept the world. The human race saw the spheres of heaven rotating and revolving through the absolute, stationary framework of space, all perfectly balanced between gravity and centrifugal force. Neptune and Pluto, two unseen planets, were calculated to exist by Newtonian principles—and were duly discovered. The laws of light and other electromagnetic waves, of chemistry and of atomic physics all came on stage, prompted to a considerable extent by problems in astronomy. The sun was proved to be no more central to the cosmic plan than the earth had been before it, but sailing with all its planetary retinue toward the constellation of Cygnus. The center of its orbit turned out to be the hub of a vast wheel of stars which is sometimes, overweeningly, called "our" galaxy, and at other times simply the Milky Way. Beyond the unimaginable dimensions of this system, millions of similar galaxies were discovered, so far away that light from the nearest started traveling toward the earth when Homo sapiens was not yet sapient.

Even before man knew of these other galaxies or realized the enormous distances with which he had to cope, Newton's beautiful equations had begun to falter and, like the Greek geometries before them, to seem no more than approximations. The facts that defeated them had to do with the propagation of light and other electromagnetic radiation through the stationary space that Newton had visualized. By redefining the nature of space and by clarifying and extending Newton's other assumptions, Albert Einstein (1879-1955) managed to rewrite classical mechanics and to correct its equations according to the new facts about light. In doing so, he predicted several phenomena that were observed only a few years later and served to confirm his theory of relativity.

Perhaps relativity, too, will have to be corrected eventually for increasingly large phenomena, just as it has already corrected Newtonian mechanics. Certainly, modern man, discovering himself halfway between the Archimedean-sized extremes of the atom and the cosmos, cannot afford to be dogmatic about his medium-sized insights. But the changes made in Newton's classical picture by Einstein's relativity have been small and sophisticated—more in the nature of improvements than of revolutionary overthrow. Modern astronomers can confidently predict that our present picture of the universe, explained in the rest of this book, is fundamentally correct.

THIS does not mean that astronomy is anywhere near being completed. Today's astronomers and tomorrow's astronauts are like citizens of a single village who have learned the size and shape of the earth but still have all its forests, deserts, peaks, shores, glaciers, caverns and ocean floors to explore. Newton himself expressed perfectly the point of view that all his successors try to emulate. "I do not know what I may appear to the world," he wrote late in his life, "but to myself I seem to have been only like a boy playing on the seashore, and diverting myself in now and then finding a smoother pebble or a prettier shell than ordinary, whilst the great ocean of truth lay all undiscovered before me."

SUN, MOON AND PLANETS CIRCLE THE ALL-IMPORTANT EARTH IN THIS MEDIEVAL FRENCH CONCEPT OF A UNIVERSE BOUNDED BY THE ZODIAC

The Mysterious Heavens

Long ago, to man's naked, primitive eye, it seemed simple: he was
the pivot around which the universe wheeled. The majestic movements of stars and planets were ordained for him alone, to guide
and warn him as he toiled and traveled. Gradually new ideas and
new measuring tools forced the truth on him: he and his world
were flecks of dust in a universe incredibly big and unknowable.

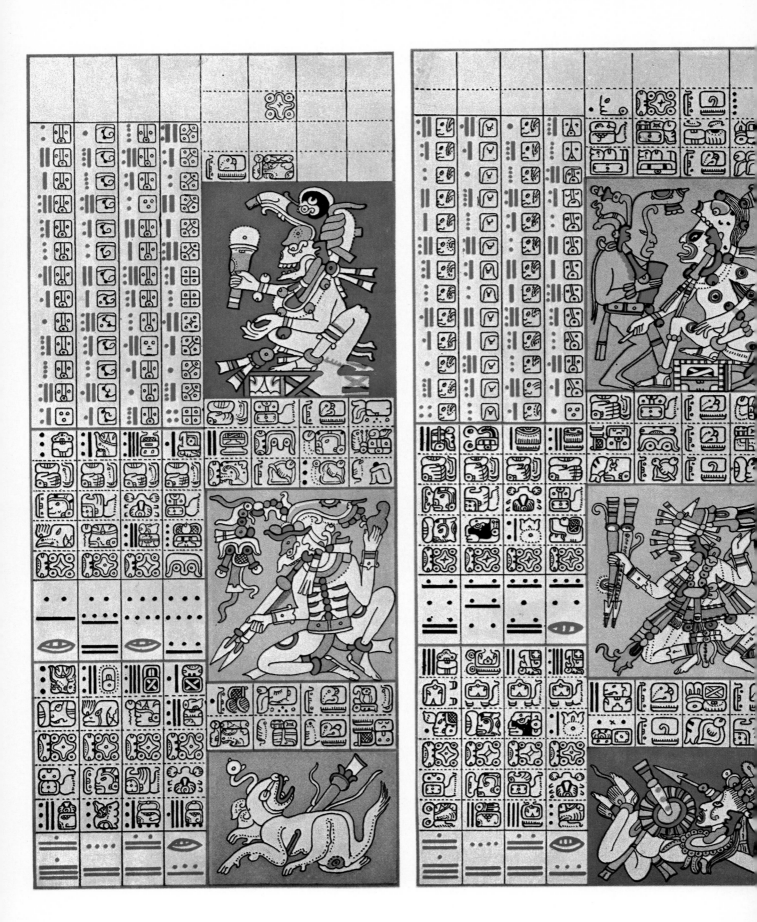

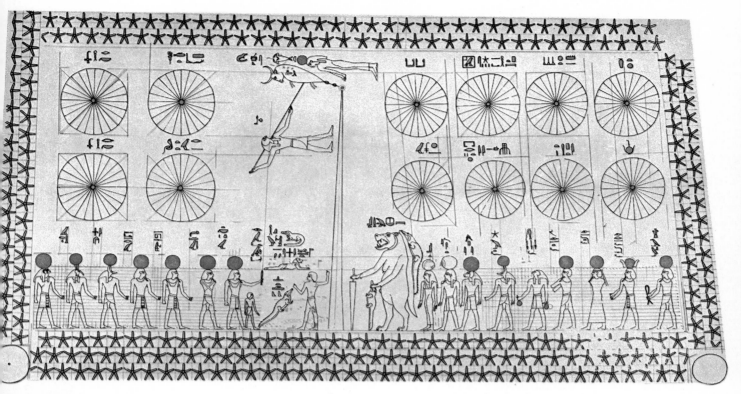

EGYPTIAN FEAST DAYS are indicated as spoked circles on this tomb decoration dating from about 1500 B.C. They are in three groups, showing feasts which occurred during the flood season (four circles at top right), the winter, or planting season (the four at left), and the summer, or harvest season. The figures at the top center represent constellations in the northern sky.

Ancient Readings of the Sky

The study of astronomy began when man, in his curiosity, made a significant discovery about celestial movements: they measured time. The sun fixed day and night and the sequence of the seasons. The moon and stars told the passage of the nighttime hours. Calendars based on these regular cycles were devised in Babylon and Egypt long before 2500 B.C. The Egyptians divided their crop year into three seasons (*above*) and always marked its beginning when the star Sirius appeared at a certain spot in the eastern sky. When Sirius showed up, it meant the Nile was about to flood. Much later the Maya of Central America used solar observations to set the time for burning off their cornfields before each year's planting, and checked their calendar against measurements of the motions of Venus (*opposite*).

MAYA MANUSCRIPT, one of three in existence (*opposite*), deals with the motions of Venus over a 104-year period. The figures at the top of the two pages are sky gods. The middle two are angry gods about to kill either the sun or Venus, and the two dead figures represent either the sun in eclipse or Venus during an invisible phase. The date of the manuscript is uncertain: it is placed between the Fourth and Eighth Centuries A.D.

THE TOWER OF BABEL, represented on this 16th Century Italian dish, was the Old Testament's way of explaining early Babylonian structures which served not only as temples but also as observatories for watching the heavens. Priest-astronomers fixed the start of each month by watching for the new moon's appearance. In the changing positions of the planets and stars, they saw omens which they used to foretell the course of the future.

19

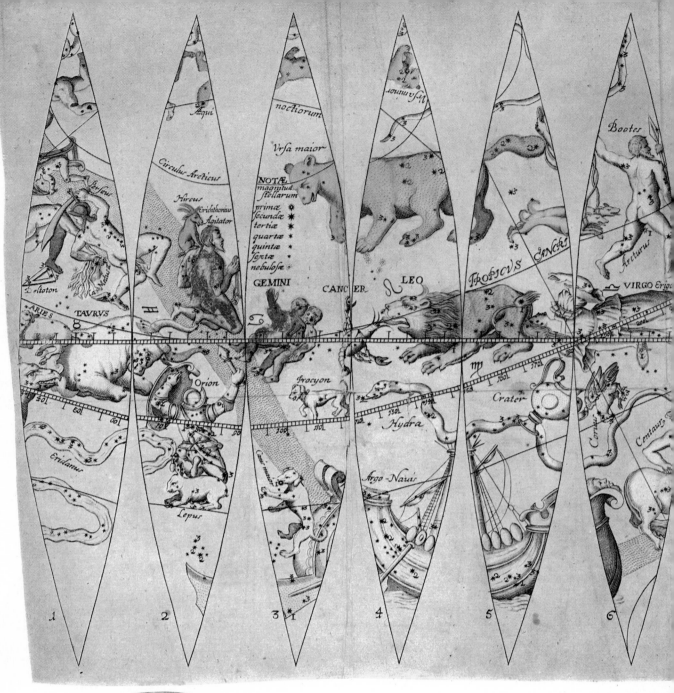

THE ZODIAC is a narrow section of the sky along which the sun moves, and which contains the 12 zodiacal signs. Named in capitals in this 17th Century Czech drawing, they follow the sun's path, shown here as a straight line. The curved lines show the equator and the two Tropics.

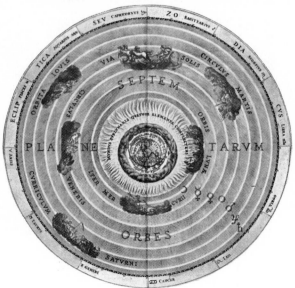

THE PTOLEMAIC SYSTEM, shown in this 17th Century Dutch illustration, plots the orbits of the moon, Mercury, Venus, the sun, Mars, Jupiter and Saturn surrounded by the stars. It erred in assuming the earth to be stationary in the center and all heavenly motions to be circular.

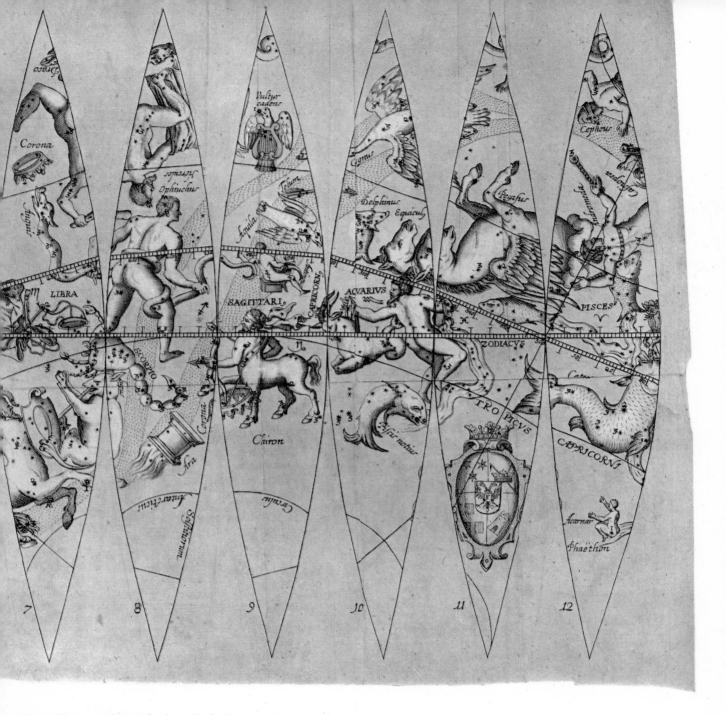

The Emerging Celestial Patterns

It did not take early sky watchers long to realize that the arrangement of the heavens was not chaotic but had a systematic pattern. The stars hung in the sky in fixed groups, and certain groups in succession always came up in the east just before sunrise. Astronomers deduced that these constellations stretched in a belt around the circle of the heavens, and that the sun, in its apparent annual trip about the earth, always stayed within that belt. The belt constellations eventually were given names and be-

came the 12 figures, or signs, of the zodiac. The zodiac was used, and still is, by astrologers, to foretell events in the lives of men and nations.

A different sort of celestial pattern was worked out by Greek astronomers in an attempt to explain the heavenly movements. This concept, perfected by Ptolemy, saw the sun, moon and planets moving around the earth in complex orbits. Ingenious and well-supported by the evidence of men's eyes, the Ptolemaic theory prevailed for another 13 centuries.

Stargazers of the East

Though science was all but blotted out in Europe during the Dark Ages, the world's accumulation of knowledge about astronomy was not lost. Both in India (from about A.D. 250) and in the Moslem world (starting four centuries later), astronomers kept on observing and calculating—and finding nothing to contradict Ptolemy's theories. Through the centuries they kept on refining all the basic instruments of naked-eye observation, such as the astrolabe for measuring stars' positions and the gnomon, or sundial, which shows the sun's movement by shadows.

Knowledge gained at observatories in Alexandria and Baghdad was carried westward to Europe and eastward to China. In India, meanwhile, astronomical efforts reached a monumental peak with the work of the 18th Century astronomer Jai Singh II, who realized that the larger his observational instruments were, the more accurate they would be. He built the structures shown here, the biggest and perhaps the best ever made for naked-eye observations.

A BRONZE DRAGON decorates an armillary sphere erected in Peking in 1674. Instruments in the observatory there were greatly refined by the Belgian Jesuit missionary Ferdinand Verbiest.

JAIPUR OBSERVATORY, known as Yantra, is the largest of five built by Jai Singh II, Maharaja of Jaipur. The structures shown here, erected in 1734, provided fixed angles to check the stars' positions. Singh hoped to improve the Indian calendar by obtaining accurate measurements of celestial motions, but he did not finish the project, and one observatory was never completed.

DELHI OBSERVATORY was built by Jai Singh II in 1724. The 56-foot-high triangle is a gnomon, or sundial. It casts a shadow on masonry arcs calibrated in hours, minutes and seconds. The sunken bowl at its foot was marked with circles of celestial longitude and latitude. A perforated metal disk held over the bowl cast a pin point of light inside, and indicated the sun's position.

Astronomical Time-Telling

One thing that limited medieval astronomers was the very elastic concept of time that most societies had. The day was divided conveniently enough into 12 hours, measured from the time the sun came up to when it set. The trouble was that an hour in a midsummer day was a good deal longer than an hour in midwinter. Further, the only timekeepers were sundials—useless on cloudy days—and even less precise devices that operated by water power. This state of affairs was increasingly bothersome to astronomers who, by the 16th Century, had begun to need accurate timing for their observations.

Fortunately the metalworking and mechanical skills of Renaissance craftsmen were beginning to produce clocks for noblemen and scientists. In 1362, Giovanni de Dondi finished an astronomical clock that not only told time but also recorded the movements of the planets with an extraordinarily complicated gear train. De Dondi's masterpiece, the oldest known European mechanical clock, was the forerunner of a clockwork revolution which, in a few centuries, was producing beautiful instruments like those seen opposite.

RTISANS' TRIUMPHS made in 16th and 17th entury Europe, these objects are at the Metropolitan Museum of Art in New York. From the p, clockwise: an Austrian astronomical globe cturing the heavens; a French perpetual calenr, or nocturnal, for telling time by observation the stars; a German sundial with a compass; an tronomical watch of English make with Lioges enamel; a book-shaped watch of German ake; a German astronomical clock with alarm.

DE DONDI'S CLOCK, 50 inches high, is seen here in a replica made for the Smithsonian Institution in Washington. The upper dials trace, from left, movements of Mars, the sun and Venus; the lower dial is a 24-hour clock. De Dondi spent 16 years on the original.

TYCHO'S CELESTIAL GLOBE, made of wood sheathed with brass, measured almost five feet across. On it were plotted the positions of 1,000 stars. The green canopy was a dust cover.

TYCHO'S EQUATORIAL ARMILLARY, nearly nine feet across, was the most accurate instrument developed up to its time (1585) for measuring the celestial latitude and longitude of stars.

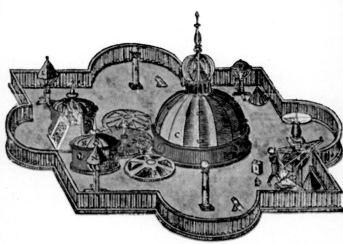

THE "STAR CASTLE" WAS PART OF TYCHO'S DANISH OBSERVATORY

The Copernican Revolt

In the 16th Century the work of two men helped destroy the Ptolemaic idea of an earth-centered universe which had been accepted everywhere for 1,300 years. In 1543 Nicholas Copernicus, a brilliant Polish lawyer and astronomer, turned the old idea around by insisting that "in the center of everything the sun must reside . . . where he can give light to all the planets." Although Copernicus mistakenly assumed that the planets followed perfect-circle orbits, still, all the facts then known about the solar system were much more simply explained by his sun-centered theory than by Ptolemy's. The old ideas died hard, however, and not until the next century was the revolutionary concept accepted.

What ultimately was to be vital to the proof of the Copernican system was the work of a Danish astronomer, Tycho Brahe. Unlike Copernicus, Tycho was a measurer rather than a theoretician, and he designed astronomical instruments larger and more carefully engineered than any that had ever been used before. Some of them are shown here. He built a remarkable observatory in 1576 and spent 21 years there making observations and calculations of the stars and planets with astonishing precision. Tycho himself clung to an earth-centered theory, but his research, in the hands of later scientists, helped to prove the new Copernican notions of the universe.

PORTRAIT OF TYCHO is framed by his "great mural quadrant (*opposite*). The man at right measures a star's altitude by sighing along a line from the eyepiece through the hole at top left

KEPLER'S STUDY in Prague still holds his telescope, a copy of Copernicus' *On the Revolutions of the Celestial Orbs* with annotations by Tycho, and some of Kepler's mathematical tables.

THE COPERNICAN SYSTEM, with the sun at the center and circled by the planets, is diagramed in this Dutch engraving of 1660. Jupiter's four moons, first seen by Galileo, are at the right.

Enter the Telescope

When Galileo turned his primitive telescope to the sky in 1609, he saw things which men had hardly dreamed were there. He found mountains on the moon; he soon saw that Venus had moonlike phases which proved its sun-centered orbit. With that, the old, comforting idea of a centrally located earth was doomed. Meanwhile in Prague, mathematician Johannes Kepler, using Tycho Brahe's measurements, calculated the planets' elliptical orbits about the sun, and upset the old concept of the circle as the typical celestial form. By observation and deduction, Kepler framed the basic laws of the solar system as it is known now, and shaped astronomy's future.

SEXTANTS AND GLOBE of the late 16th Century stand on porch outside Kepler's study in Prague's Belvedere Castle, whe he worked with Tycho. St. Vitus' Cathedral is in the backgrou

2

Probing
the Universe

WHEN Newton died, bequeathing to science the fundamental guidance and assurance of his equations, the future of astronomy looked straightforward and simple. Stargazers had only to work out the details of the cosmic plan by filling in the unknowns in Newton's equations. They would grind larger lenses for their telescopes and machine finer sextants for the measurement of celestial geometry: with these they would determine all the masses and motions of the solar system and go on to study all the stars beyond. For almost two centuries, young astronomers could hope—as did Sir William Herschel (1738-1822), the discoverer of the planet Uranus—that they would succeed in "surveying the entire heavens" and "ascertaining the plan of their general structure." Fortunately for astronomy, which is far richer than it might have been otherwise, their optimistic ambitions and their thirst for quick solutions were repeatedly frustrated. The great frustrater was light.

The unruly nature of light had been glimpsed even before Newton's day. Indeed, Newton met and conquered one of the major challenges that light posed to telescope makers. This was the problem of chromatic aberration, caused by the way light spreads out into a rainbow when it passes through a prism or

Galileo Galilei (1564-1642), an Italian astronomer, made telescopic observations which confirmed the Copernican sun-centered idea of our solar system. The Inquisition feared his discoveries and forced him to give up his astronomical studies.

Sir Isaac Newton (1642-1727), an English physicist who profoundly influenced 18th Century thought, formulated the laws of gravity, invented the reflecting telescope and discovered how a prism resolves white light into many different spectral colors.

other wedge-shaped sheet of glass. The early telescopes were all lens instruments—of the type called refractors today—essentially magnifying glasses at the ends of tubes. In the simplest refractor, the main lens collects the light and bends it to a focal point, while the second lens, the eyepiece, enlarges the collected image. The collecting lens can be several thousand square inches in area and so can gather in far more light than the scant .03-square-inch area of an unaided eye. Unfortunately, however, a lens also acts as a prism, bending the different colors of light—the different wave lengths—by different amounts. The short, energetic waves of blue light are bent more than the longer, more listless waves of red light. As a consequence, the blue light focuses sooner after passing through the lens than the red light does. "White" starlight, containing light of all wave lengths or colors, is focused in separate images; neither the blue one nor the red one is sharp because out-of-focus rays from the others fuzz it up.

ONE way to minimize this peculiarity of light is to shape the lens so that it will focus all wave lengths as far beyond the lens as possible. Before Newton's time, telescopes with long focal lengths were the only solution. The most extreme designs—called aerial telescopes—dispensed with tubes altogether. The main lens was simply strung up on the top of a pole and the astronomer sat a hundred feet or more below it with his eyepiece. Johannes Hevelius (1611-1687), who mapped the moon, used an aerial telescope 150 feet long—equal to the height of a modern 12-story building. Christiaan Huygens (1629-1695), first to construct a pendulum-regulated clock and the first man to see that the rings of Saturn really were rings and not ill-focused moons, built aerial telescopes as much as 210 feet long.

Ungainly instruments like these were not for Newton. His solution to the problem of chromatic aberration was to perfect a totally new type of telescope, the reflector. In a reflecting telescope, the main light-collector is not a lens at all, but a curved mirror. Nowadays, the surface of a glass mirror is covered with a fine coating of metal—usually aluminum—so that starlight falling on it does not penetrate the glass but rebounds instantly. In this way chromatic aberration never has a chance to take place and all the wave lengths of light bouncing from the mirror are equally bent by its curvature. The kind of curvature needed to focus the parallel rays from a star is parabolic, the same shape as the reflector in a car's headlight. The headlight, of course, reverses the process: instead of gathering outside light into a focus, it beams the light from a focal electric bulb in parallel rays onto the road ahead.

Since the parabolic mirror at the lower end of a Newtonian telescope tube simply bounces the light of a star back again, some means has to be used to intercept the image before it escapes. In Newton's original telescope, this was done by a small, flat mirror mounted obliquely near the focal point to flash the light out sideways to the astronomer through a hole in the tube. One might think that hanging this second mirror directly in the beam of incoming starlight would cast shadows or cause distortion, but instead it simply dims the starlight slightly. Indeed, in the largest modern reflectors the astronomer himself, with his photographic plates and all his gear, is often hung in the beam, interposed between the star he is studying and the great mirror where he sees the star reflected. An alternative to putting the astronomer in the beam or reflecting the image out the side of the tube is to bounce the image back downward through a hole in the parabolic mirror itself. Most of the large modern telescopes incorporate at least two of these ways of getting the image out of the tube. Once outside, the light is often processed still further, through more mirrors and lenses, slits, prisms, filters or vacuum tubes, so that the astronomer can single out the parts he is studying.

Parabolic mirrors did not prove to be the only solution to light's chromatic aberration. By the middle of the 18th Century, optical craftsmen devised combinations of lenses for refracting telescopes which aimed at canceling out the prism effect, at least for wave lengths of light to which the human eye is most sensitive. In today's astronomy, of course, the human eye has been largely superseded by photography—by all sorts of films and filters which register light outside the normal visual range and bring out latent aberration in even the most ingeniously corrected lenses. Despite this problem, refracting telescopes are still definitely useful for such important tasks as measuring stellar distances, and are also used for general, exploratory observation. Moreover, many astronomers say that no one has felt the full thrill of stargazing until he has looked directly at the heavens through one of the giant, classical refractors. The largest refracting telescope today—and in many ways the most impressive-looking telescope of any sort—is the one at Yerkes Observatory in Williams Bay, Wisconsin. In this instrument, two 40-inch lenses are mounted in a 63-foot tube above a floor that rises and falls by machinery within a huge iron dome that opens and closes in segments, also by machinery.

Sir William Herschel (1738-1822) was a German-born English astronomer who constructed powerful telescopes to systematically explore the heavens. He discovered Uranus, two satellites of Saturn, and cataloged many double stars and nebulae.

IMPRESSIVE as refractors are, the workaday tools of modern astronomy are reflectors, and the prince of these is the Hale telescope—an enormous, 200-inch mirror mounted in an open, tumbler-shaped nest of metal girders within a dome a mile above sea level on California's Palomar Mountain. Like the 40-inch Yerkes refractor—and also like America's third largest telescope, the 100-inch Mount Wilson reflector—the Palomar giant was conceived by George Ellery Hale (1868-1938), one of America's greatest astronomers and unquestionably the world's greatest promoter of big telescopes. Hale started work on the 200-inch in 1928, when he raised money for preliminary design studies. After a false start on the massive mirror—parts of the mold broke off as the molten glass was being poured—a perfect 200-inch pyrex disk was finally cast late in 1934 and cooled for nearly a year. The 20-ton disk was then shipped by flatcar to Pasadena for an arduous, war-interrupted 11 years of grinding and polishing. At the end of this process, in the autumn of 1947, over five tons of glass had been worn away and 62,000 pounds of abrasive consumed in shaping the desired parabola.

During the course of the work, Hale died, but the project continued under Ira S. Bowen, the present director of the Mount Wilson and Palomar Observatories. Shy and reserved, but a man of great will power, Bowen was determined that this great telescope should be flawless. Although scores of knowledge-hungry astronomers waited, criticized, fumed and got ready to tear the stars from the sky, Bowen quietly insisted on absolute precision. Finally in 1948, with the most perfect optics and mounting of any telescope on earth, the Hale 200-inch went into use. Since then, it has done more to advance astronomy than any other instrument in the course of history—except, perhaps, Hale's 100-inch Mount Wilson reflector that preceded it, or Galileo's original, minuscule refractor.

The Earl of Rosse (1800-1867), also a British astronomer, is known chiefly for his construction of large mirrors for reflecting telescopes. His greatest instrument had a mirror six feet in diameter. It helped resolve nebulae into star groups.

What such a telescope as the 200-inch means to knowledge is easy to appreciate from the discoveries which have been made because of other instrument developments in the past. Ptolemy, when he perfected the Almagest in Second Century Alexandria, had no basic instruments except shadow-casting gnomons and angle-measuring sextants. Without the invention of Galileo's wobbling, hand-held "optick glass," the ideas of Copernicus might well have fallen into the same oblivion as the Copernican insights of Eratosthenes long before. Without Tycho Brahe's improvements in the size and precision of angle-measuring instruments, Kepler would never have had the exact information necessary for unveiling the laws of the solar system. When Friedrich Wilhelm Bessel, early in the 19th Century, built an observatory for the King of Prussia in Königsberg and furnished it with instruments more modern and precise than any that had been made before, he was able to measure the first distances to nearby stars. In 1845, England's William Parsons, third Earl of Rosse, finished building a 72-inch reflector—the largest and the last of the metal mirrors—inside a 52-foot tube on the grounds of his Irish feudal estate, Birr Castle. With his "leviathan of Parsonstown," as the locals called it, he was able to discover the structure of spiral galaxies that we now know to lie outside our own Milky Way. As for the 200-inch, when it began looking out from Palomar it brought billions of hitherto unobserved stars and remote galaxies within man's ken.

O VER the centuries, big telescopes have been set up at famous European observatories near Paris, London, Rome, Königsberg and Leningrad. They are all over the United States: on the East Coast, the West Coast, in mid-continent and among the ideally arid heights of the Southwest. To survey the stars of the southern sky, other observatories have been built in South Africa and Australia. Meanwhile, astronomers have devised more and more meticulous mountings for their instruments so that the telescopes now can track their targets accurately despite the daily rotation of the earth. The 200-inch Hale works so precisely that Milton Humason, one of modern astronomy's finest observers, has been able to keep it trained on stars for the purpose of making long-exposure photographs for as much as seven hours, and get pinpoint-sharp pictures. What is more, those hours of exposure were not continuous, but spread over a week, interrupted seven or eight times by intervening hours of daylight.

With precision mounts like these, astronomers further refine the aim of their telescopes with push-button controls that center the big tubes on cross hairs only a few thousandths of an inch in diameter. Nor are photographic plates the only recording devices employed: the target images that the telescopes collect are subject to analysis by spectroscopy and by photometry and by the micrometric measurements of angular distances. All of this endeavor has as its purpose a single object—the avaricious accumulation of facts.

Every piece of astronomical evidence is like one of the bricks in a delicate, openwork wall: each brick is supported by hundreds of others and helps to support as many more. The whole structure of interlocked, intellectual interpretation rests on strict logic of brain-twisting subtlety. The logic, in its turn, is supported by facts and figures that have been determined with eye-twisting precision. At the foundation of the structure, supporting everything else, is the same universal phenomenon of nature: light—the many-eyed messenger of the universe.

Some of the uses of light are comparatively simple and straightforward. For example, the only direct way to measure how far away the lights of the stars are in the sky is by a trick of geometry known as parallax. Parallax is

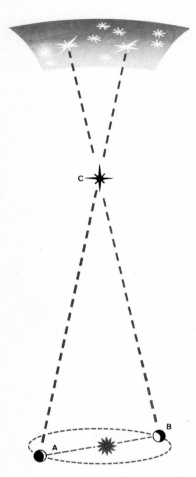

The apparent movement of stars, actually a reflection of the earth's motion as viewed against the background of more distant stars, is known as parallax, and is used by astronomers to calculate distances. If star C is viewed first from point A on the earth's orbit, then six months later from point B, it will appear to have moved with respect to stars farther away behind it. This apparent movement makes it possible to calculate the angles at points A and B. From that, the distance to point C can be determined by trigonometry, since the distance across the earth's orbit from point A to point B is already known.

a measure of the amount by which an object seems to move, in relation to its background when an observer looks at it from two different places. Anyone can judge the parallax of something very near to him—say, a candle on a table, in relation to the wall—simply by looking at it first with one eye, and then with the other. In the same way, an astronomer can see the parallax of a planet by sighting it, against the backdrop of stars, at different times on one night as the rotation of the earth conveniently shifts his telescope a few thousand miles to a new sighting position. So, too, he has learned to measure the parallax of some 6,000 of the nearest stars by looking at them during opposite seasons of the year when the earth's revolution around the sun has given him a base line 186 million miles long.

T HE nearest stars are so far away that even a base line of 186 million miles is still embarrassingly short. After centuries of attempts by other astronomers, Bessel in 1838 finally measured the parallax of 61 Cygni, one of the nearest stars. The parallactic displacement he saw, back and forth over the sky every six months, was an angle of only .3 second—three tenths of a 60th of a 60th of a 360th of a full circle. Yet this gnat's whisker of measurement means that 61 Cygni is 65 trillion miles away from the earth. For simplicity's sake, astronomers call this distance 11 light-years—a light-year being the distance light travels in a year, or six trillion miles.

Within months of Bessel's great measurement, Thomas Henderson in South Africa had found that Alpha Centauri is the sun's nearest neighbor—now known to be only 4.3 light-years away—and Friedrich Wilhelm Struve in Russia (the great-grandfather of Otto Struve who, until 1961, was director of the National Radio Astronomy Observatory in Green Bank, West Virginia) had found the distance to Vega—now known to be 27 light-years. Beyond a distance of some 400 light-years—where the angle of parallax falls below 0.008 second—these geometric means of measurement are essentially useless.

Eventually, astronomers may be able to measure parallaxes of more distant stars, or even of remote galaxies, by taking advantage of the sun's own revolution around the hub of the Milky Way. But since it takes 100 million years for the sun to go halfway round the hub, the results will not be in for some time. In the meanwhile, astronomers have learned to measure distances beyond the range of parallax by other methods, which depend, in their turn, on other peculiarities of light. The light from stars within parallactic range has revealed that some stars belong to certain clearly defined and easily recognizable classes which always have the same real brightness. When other stars of the same sort are found beyond the range of parallax, astronomers can estimate their distance by the decrease in their brightness. Checked by all sorts of theoretical calculations about how stars burn and what makes them bright, this method has served to measure cosmic distances of millions of light-years—millions of millions of millions of miles.

Classifying the stars so as to judge their distances—and their motions and masses—involved new understandings of light's properties: qualities of seeming unruliness and actual consistency that Newton had never suspected. One such unruliness was discovered in 1814 by the German optician, Joseph von Fraunhofer. Newton had shown that white sunlight, bent apart by a prism, becomes a rainbow of all the colors. But Fraunhofer found that the sun's spectrum was not a perfect rainbow but instead was slashed by

LIGHT DISTORTION

Chromatic aberration occurs when light which is made up of many different wave lengths splits as it passes through a single lens. Because of its shorter waves, the blue light is bent more than, and focused closer to the lens than the longer red light. This lens characteristic makes sharp focusing impossible in single-lens telescopes.

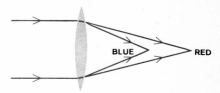

Converging lens (or positive type) bends the light toward the lens's center of focus, with the blue focus point nearer the lens.

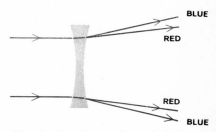

Diverging lens (or negative type) bends the light away from the center of focus. Blue light bends away more than the red.

Lens systems, when corrected for each other, focus light at the same point. Modern telescopes combine lenses for sharp focus.

hundreds of dark lines. Fraunhofer carefully plotted the locations of as many of these lines as he could see—today they are numbered in the thousands—but he had no idea what they meant. It was more than 40 years before studies showed that the light emitted by common elements, when made white-hot in the laboratory, showed bright slashes in their spectra and that these slashes perfectly matched the lines of darkness Fraunhofer had discovered.

Today, all this is understood in terms of atomic theory. Each element—or kind of atom—can emit and absorb energy only at the specific wave lengths dictated by its atomic structure. In the spectrum of an incandescent substance, the bright lines are produced by atoms emitting energy at their prescribed wave lengths. In the spectrum of the sun, the dark lines are produced by the action of elements in the solar atmosphere that absorb radiation at their prescribed wave lengths. In the mid-19th Century, when this explanation was unknown, absorption and emission lines in the spectrum brought about an intensive investigation that was finally crowned by the discovery of light's true nature and of its place among other forms of energy.

THE realization which led to a clearer concept of light, and to much of modern physics, was that visible light makes up only a tiny fraction of the whole spectrum. Above the brightest visible blues in the spectrum are shorter, invisible ultraviolet waves, X rays and, finally, gamma rays of infinitesimal trillionth-of-an-inch wave length. Below the darkest visible reds are the longer, invisible infrareds, microwaves, radio waves and—newly discovered—"micropulsations" which reach wave lengths of millions of miles. Finding that all these waves had a part in a single electromagnetic spectrum was due to many men, principally to the Englishman Michael Faraday (1791-1867), who did the experimental work, and the Scot James Clerk Maxwell (1831-1879), who wrapped the entire electromagnetic phenomenon in equations and made it almost as clear as Newton had made mechanics and the motions of planets.

Out of Faraday and Maxwell—and out of the atomic theory that grew from their insights—astronomy developed a whole new kind of post-Newtonian study which is usually described as astrophysics. "There are some things," declared the French philosopher Auguste Comte (1798-1857), "of which the human race must remain forever in ignorance, for example the chemical constitution of the heavenly bodies." But astrophysics, which made spectacular advances after Maxwell's publication of *Treatise on Electricity and Magnetism* in 1873, proved Comte many times wrong. Already in 1859 the German Gustav Kirchhoff (1824-1887) had identified some of the sun's principal spectral lines with elements in its atmosphere. By 1871, the English astronomer Sir Joseph Norman Lockyer was so sure of the interpretation of the spectral lines that he announced the discovery of a new chemical element, completely unknown on earth, which he christened "the sun element," helium. Fourteen years later, the Scotsman Sir William Ramsay discovered that helium, in minute traces, does exist on earth in association with radioactive substances.

Spectroscopes that fanned out the peacock tails of starlight were soon being used in every major observatory on earth. In early models, the fanning was done by prisms, in later models by diffraction gratings of lines closely ruled on glass. Either way, the white radiance of the cosmos could be shattered into rainbows, revealing by their spectral lines the identity of atoms pulsating billions of miles away. Over the years, the spectral lines proved to hold amazing quantities of other information, too: the speed of a star moving toward or away from the

TWO KINDS OF TELESCOPES

A reflector (opposite) and a refractor telescope (below) differ from each other in that a reflector operates with a system of mirrors, while a refractor uses a system of lenses. Refractors are the older type of the two and employ the same principle as field glasses and microscopes. Reflectors bounce light from a parabolic mirror at the bottom of a tube to either a small mirror near the top, which carries it to an eyepiece outside, or to an observer in a carriage set within the tube of the telescope itself.

A refractor telescope gathers light through an "objective" lens at the top of its long tube, bends the rays and then carries them to the eyepiece, where they are focused by a series of magnifying lenses. Unlike the reflector telescopes, light passes through a refractor's tube a single time. Refractors were first used extensively by Galileo.

solar system, the rapidity of a star's rotation, the temperature of its surface, the strength of its magnetic field, even the amount of invisible gas drifting in space between it and the earth.

About the same time as the invention of the spectroscope—in 1850 in fact—photographic plates were first exposed to the stars by John Whipple at the suggestion of William Bond, director of the Harvard College Observatory. Because they were permanent records, with a persuasiveness and an objectivity that no astronomer's sketch or verbal description could match, plates quickly replaced the astronomer's eye as the main means of observation. Soon they were recording not only such rarities as comets and eclipses but also the routine of star fields and star spectra.

Objectivity, while eminently desirable, was not the sole nor even the most important attribute of photographic astronomy. A fundamental difference exists between the human eye and the photographic plate: whether an astronomer stares at a distant star field for a minute or all night long, his eye senses no more light in a vigil than it does in a wink. The photographic plate, on the contrary, collects light in a cumulative process: a 10-second exposure may reveal 20 fairly bright stars, but a 10-hour exposure will show 2,000 or more stars that are too faint to be seen by naked eye even when assisted by the finest telescope in the world.

Today, everything has become a matter of photographic record, subject to re-examination and remeasurement by future generations of astronomers. At the same time, so many other technical refinements have been added that an astronomer's gear can seem almost as complex as the heavens themselves: new films, filters and developers; blinkers to flip back and forth between plates of the same part of the sky taken at different times which make both short- and long-term changes easy to see; electronic scanning techniques to sift photographs and pick out those with anything new on them; telescopes, called Schmidts, which turn combinations of spherical mirrors and corrective lenses into what are really giant, wide-angle cameras; all sorts of other mirror-and-lens combinations for special, restricted purposes; and even computer programs that permit telescopes to keep robot-watch over assigned stars.

WHILE technology is taking the guesswork and the eyestrain out of classical astronomy, there remains another revolution that has hardly begun. This is the examination of the heavens in some of the other wave lengths of radiation that Faraday and Maxwell proved to exist outside the narrow spectrum of visible light. The first scientific explorer to venture into this unknown ocean of knowledge was Karl Jansky at the Bell Telephone Laboratories in the late 1920s and early 1930s. All that the youthful Jansky had to work with at the start was unexplained static in transoceanic radiotelephone links. He had the purely practical assignment of finding out where the static came from so that the telephone company could minimize it. But Jansky was a more than purely practical person, and when the source of the static proved difficult to pinpoint, he went beyond the normal call of duty in his efforts to track it down. He built an unprecedented radio antenna 60 feet long and mounted it on four old wheels on a circular cinder-block track. The contraption looked like nothing so much as an outsized Wright brothers' airplane with all the silk torn off the wings. But by carefully rotating this Rube Goldbergism and collecting volumes of graphic data on the radio signals it received, he was finally able to divide up the static of one important short-wave frequency into three categories: bangs

The Newtonian focus (point N) is an arrangement in a reflector by which light is bounced from a parabolic mirror to a focal point near the top of the tube, where a small flat mirror deflects it out through a hole in the tube's side. The prime focus arrangement (point P) has no second mirror and light is focused in the instrument.

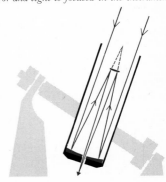

The Cassegrainian focus is an arrangement by which light is collected on a parabolic mirror at the bottom of the tube. The light is then reflected to a smaller curved mirror near the top of the tube, where it is aimed back through a hole in the center of the big bottom mirror and brought to focus at a point below the telescope itself.

The coudé focus is yet another type of arrangement, much like the Cassegrainian. Also found in the reflector telescopes, it is used exclusively for spectroscopy. Rather than permit the light to pass through a hole, the coudé deflects it with a flat mirror, carries it outside the tube and onto the lenses and gratings of the spectrograph.

from nearby thunderclaps, clicks from distant thunderclaps and a steady whisper from outer space. He published his results in 1932.

Jansky's whisper was nothing less than the strong radio noise that emanates from the nucleus of the Milky Way. After these pioneer studies, Jansky's subsequent work with the Bell Laboratories led him away from further pursuit of the whisper, but another young investigator, Grote Reber, took up the challenge. An engineer employed by a Chicago radio manufacturer, Reber read Jansky's report and, by 1937, was eavesdropping on the universe with the aid of a 31-foot sheet-metal dish he had assembled in his backyard. Reber not only confirmed that the galactic nucleus—invisible to optical telescopes because of obscuring clouds of dust—was a signal source, but located a number of other ''hot spots'' in the sky that did not appear to coincide with any visible objects. His first reports were published in 1940. In the war-torn world, there were few opportunities to follow up these clues. Nonetheless, Jan Oort and his colleagues at the Observatory of the University of Leiden, in occupied Holland, spent these bleak years drawing up a plan for postwar investigation of the new field. With the war's end, these and other investigators round the world set up antennae, recorded the ''noises,'' and began amassing information. It soon became apparent that Jansky, and Reber after him, had founded a whole new field of study —radio astronomy.

Today radio astronomy has developed into a full-fledged partner of classic optical astronomy. All over the world, antennae have been raised toward the stars and have begun gathering in the celestial sighs and murmurs which make up the true music of the spheres. For the fun of it, radio astronomers occasionally connect up their antennae and amplifiers with loudspeakers so that they can hear the cosmic broadcasts as audible sound waves. They say that when they do, the Milky Way hisses incessantly, the sun sighs intermittently and the planet Jupiter comes through with a deep, lugubrious grumble that sounds like the ancient Roman god of thunder himself. Actually, however, radio astronomers ''listen'' to the universe only through the graphs of signal intensity traced by their monitoring instruments as their antennae sweep the sky. By marking the strength and direction of the radio hot spots on sky maps, they have gradually accumulated a picture of the radio heavens which is altogether different from the picture of the optical heavens seen by ordinary astronomers.

Probing beyond the confines of the solar system, radio astronomers have found that the real stars are all inaudible but that the clouds of cosmic gas and dust between the stars emit radiation in a narrow band of wave lengths centered at about 21 centimeters, while other celestial objects give off signals at other frequencies, depending on such factors as their temperature and turbulence. Most numerous of all cosmic radio sources—and also the faintest—are galaxies beyond the Milky Way. Some of the ones heard by man's largest radio telescopes are thought to be more distant than the range of the best optical telescopes. They are thought, in fact, to be about 10^{23} (100,000,000,000,000,000,000,000)- miles away.

To pick out the faint voices of the celestial chorus, radio astronomers have had to lavish infinite pains on their equipment. The big and obvious part of a radio telescope is always the antenna, or energy collector. The two main kinds of antenna are the dish and the dipole array. The dish is a large, shallow parabolic ''mirror'' of sheet metal or wire mesh which gathers

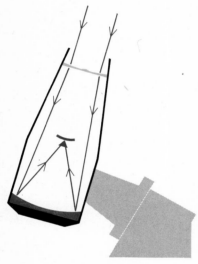

The Schmidt telescope combines features of both reflector and refractor instruments. Used solely for photographic work, the Schmidt first passes light through a lens which corrects spherical aberration, then bounces it off a large spherical (rather than parabolic) mirror to a point of focus on a curved photographic plate halfway between the lens and the big mirror.

in radio energy and concentrates it on a small antenna at the point of focus in exactly the same way that a parabolic mirror in a reflecting telescope collects light on the lens of an eyepiece. By contrast, the dipole array is a forest of many separate, identical antennae that collect energy by feeding all their weak individual signals into one common receiving set.

Dish antennae have the great advantage that they can be easily tuned to receive first one wave length and then another. Naked dipoles, on the other hand, can receive only a narrow band of wave lengths which depends on the length and spacing of the metal rods out of which they are constructed. But dipoles are easy to put up, and hundreds or even thousands of them—spaced out in grids or crosses over acres of land—can collect all the energy on one wave length with enormous acuity. When dipole arrays are used as radio telescopes, the basic antennae are usually elaborated and given extra sensitivity by spiral coils or wavy gratings of wire known in radio jargon as parasites. In some telescopes the dipoles can be rotated and tilted in unison to point in more than one direction. In others, they are all fixed immovably to the ground and can "look" only in the direction to which the spinning, orbiting earth aims them. Surprisingly enough, this is not a crippling limitation for a radio telescope. In the course of a year any point on earth has a substantial fraction of the sky directly overhead. And since neither daylight nor overcast materially interferes with radio reception, a fixed dipole array can be extremely useful for carrying out comprehensive sky surveys. The movable dish antennae, in their turn, show the radio astronomer the exact—or nearly exact—direction in which the source is located.

The one great drawback of dish antennae is the cost and difficulty of building them. The largest yet constructed is the 250-foot radio mirror at Jodrell Bank near Manchester, England. This monster revolves from side to side and rocks up and down on a gigantic yoke that keeps it pointed precisely even under the stress of high winds and heavy rains. A still larger, 600-foot steerable dish planned by the U.S. Navy at Sugar Grove, West Virginia, has run up against such huge engineering cost and problems that its actual construction is now, in 1962, a dubious prospect hedged by the uncertainties of congressional appropriations and Pentagon planning. United States radio astronomers, meanwhile, are pinning their hopes on two other dishes: a 140-foot one nearing completion at Green Bank, West Virginia, and a vast nonsteerable one, 1,000 feet in diameter, which will consist of a wire mesh parabola strung out around a natural indentation in the hills of Puerto Rico. Though earth-bound, the Puerto Rican giant will be able to map part of the radio sky in a number of wave lengths with new precision and farseeing depth.

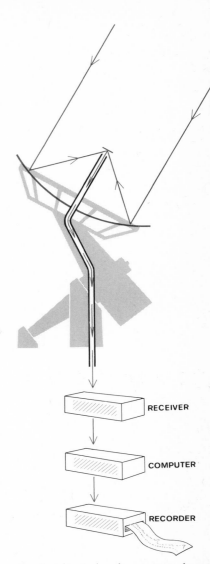

A radio telescope is a huge antenna for collecting weak radio signals from outer space. One type, shown here, uses a large dish to concentrate the waves on the antenna proper which is mounted above the center of the dish. The waves are first amplified by a receiver, then sent to a computer which sorts out static. A recorder finally transcribes the signals on a graph.

As optical telescopes are often troubled by city lights and smogs, so radio telescopes are beset by interference and noise. At a series of international conferences, radio astronomers have persuaded nations to regulate the air waves and keep commercial transmissions off the chief astronomical frequencies of nature. Even so, the radio sky remains noisy and the gurgle of the celestial spheres is often drowned out by man-made din. To weed out unwanted signals, radio astronomers feed the impulses from their antennae into powerful amplifiers which usually feed, in turn, into computers for sorting out the random space noises from the nonrandom human noises. The fidelity of all this electronic gear has to be enormously high—high enough to make the best modern-home music systems seem like Edison victrolas by comparison.

Largest of all the problems posed to radio astronomers is pinpointing the direction of what they "hear." Radio waves are a thousand to a hundred million times longer than the waves of visible light. As a result, the energy-collecting areas of radio telescopes have to be correspondingly large to be sure of the direction of what they hear. To discriminate as sharply between two close radio sources of middling wave length as the 200-inch Palomar telescope does between two close stars, a radio telescope would need a dish wider than the moon. Nevertheless, radio astronomers have found ways of being tolerably accurate.

When electromagnetic waves enter a circular opening such as the snout of a radio telescope, they alternately reinforce and dim themselves in concentric rings known as an interference pattern. Two radio telescopes miles apart, by focusing on the same radio source and making its interference patterns coincide, can vastly refine their measurement of the direction of the source they are tuned in on. Together they can begin to act like a radio dish as wide as the distance between them. One of the most ambitious schemes for taking advantage of this interference effect is being undertaken jointly by the governments of Holland and Belgium. When eventually realized in steel and electricity, each arm of a gigantic cross will stretch three miles, and the 100 steerable antennae in the array—all acting in unison—will form a single radio telescope of immense power and precision.

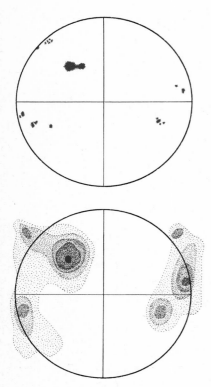

Two simultaneous views of sunspots show how different they look through an optical telescope (top) and a radio telescope (bottom). The radio telescope does not "see" in the literal sense, but records the radio waves emanating from the sunspot. When these are plotted, they give details about the strength and extent of sunspot activity that cannot be obtained optically. The different patterns in this diagram indicate different intensities of radiation, growing stronger toward the center of each sunspot. The areas extending beyond the edge of the sun show activity taking place on the curve of the sun's surface and beyond the conventional view of the optical telescopes.

THE ingenious techniques of radio astronomy have already revealed many things that are hidden from ordinary light-gathering telescopes: unlit clouds of interstellar gas, and galaxies so far away that they may never be detected except by radio. And yet these new horizons that radio astronomy is opening up are narrow indeed. They represent only one of the many invisible portions of the electromagnetic spectrum. Radio waves, like the light waves of classic astronomy, come to earth because our atmosphere is transparent to their wave lengths. But the universe shines in scores of other wave lengths ranging the gamut of the spectrum—and to most of these the atmosphere is an opaque barrier. To map the universe in these many "lights," man is beginning to loft new kinds of telescopes above the blanket of the earth's air. Balloons have gone up 82,000 feet to photograph the sun in ultraviolet light. Rockets carrying ultraviolet sensors have been swamped by the unexpected blue brilliance of the stars. Explorer XI orbited a gamma-ray telescope for looking at the center of the Milky Way in the high-frequency waves emanating from atomic nuclei. At the opposite ends of the electromagnetic spectrum, short X rays and the longest of cosmic radio wave lengths have not yet been "seen" at all.

Sorting out the many lights of the sky and putting them all together again in their meaningful brilliance will undoubtedly require an observatory outside the earth's atmosphere. Automatic orbiting observatories which will relay their findings to earth are on their way to the pad and the first such—for solar studies—has already been launched. But ultimately the future of astronomy probably lies on the airless moon, where low gravity and lack of winds will permit radio telescopes to be built with mirrors hundreds of miles wide, and where entirely new kinds of "optick glasses" can focus and record even the most arcane hue of the electromagnetic spectrum.

ABOVE A LOOMING RADIO TELESCOPE THE STARS CIRCLE THE NORTH POLE, LOOKING LIKE BRIGHT STREAKS IN THIS 90-MINUTE TIME EXPOSURE

Astronomy's Tools

The secrets of the universe are written largely in light. Through the centuries astronomers have constantly devised newer, better receivers for these messages. They refined the telescope from the first crude lenses of Galileo's day to the marvel of Palomar, broke white light into fact-filled fragments and have now added a powerful partner, the radio telescope, that searches beyond light's range.

A CROWDED ROOFTOP in Danzig was the observatory of Johannes Hevelius, pioneer of lunar topography. He also studied distant objects but learned little because of dust and other substances in the atmosphere.

A DANISH GENIUS, Ole Roemer, proved that light has a finite speed. His fixed meridian telescope, shown here, which moved vertically but not horizontally, was used in timing the exact motions of planets and stars.

A TOUR DE FORCE in telescope construction was Lord Rosse's "Leviathan of Parsonstown." His reflector was enormous but often frustrated by Irish weather; its great discovery was the shape of spiral nebulae.

In Pursuit of Starlight

To early astronomers, the nature of light was a mystery, the lack of it a constant frustration. Without the photographic plates that store up starlight for their descendants today, they worked in a vast darkness; yet their achievements were amazing. In the 17th Century Johannes Hevelius of Danzig charted the moon's face with clumsy lens telescopes *(left)*, cataloged 1,564 stars, observed sunspots and discovered four comets. His Danish contemporary Ole Roemer *(below, opposite)* demonstrated that the speed of light was not infinite by timing the eclipses of Jupiter's moons. Seeking ever to see the elusive light of the cosmos more clearly, other men designed reflecting telescopes with cast and polished mirrors of metal—an effort climaxed in 1845 by the building of Lord Rosse's bulky six-foot reflector *(below)*.

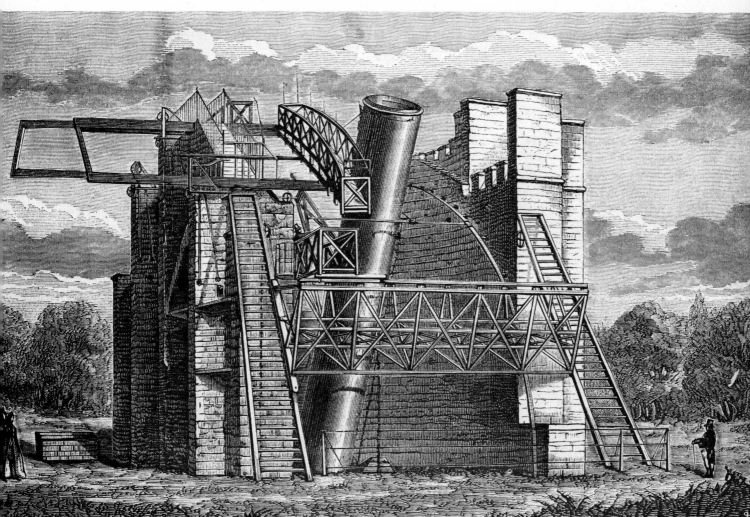

DISTANT GALAXIES, far too faint for the human eye to detect, have become visible as blobs and dots on this photographic plate after a long exposure with Palomar's giant, 200-inch telescope.

CHILLED BY DRY ICE to provide greater sensitivity, a photo-electric cell is attached to Mount Wilson's 60-inch telescope to determine the brightness and also the colors of distant stars.

Help from the Camera

Even the best telescopes were no better than the eyes of astronomers until the invention of photography. No sooner had the daguerreotype been perfected in 1839 than this new art began to revolutionize science. In 1840 John William Draper made the first feeble daguerreotype of the moon. Ten years later George Bond photographed a star for the first time. By 1857 more sensitive plates were available and photographic astronomy was on its way. Now permanent records could be kept, and old observations made years ago could be compared with recent ones to measure such things as the movement of stars.

Another important quality soon became apparent: the ability of photographic film to store up light. With sensitive film exposed for long periods of time— sometimes night after night—to the light collected by the telescope, stars far too faint for human eyes to see would slowly begin to register on the plate. Thus, even without increasing a telescope's light-gathering power, astronomers could see more than ever before. Telescopes were transformed, in fact, into cameras.

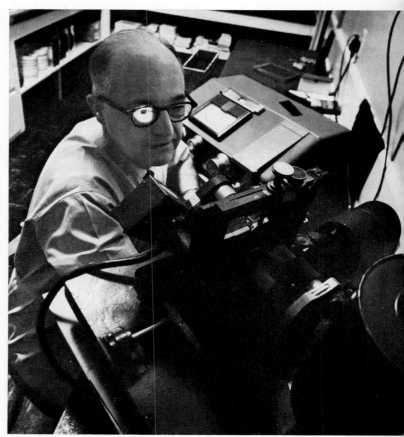

AIN DRIVE of the Mount Wilson 100-inch (*opposite*) dwarfs e late astronomer Walter S. Adams, who uses a small guide escope to adjust the huge instrument by push-button control.

FILM IS CHECKED by Palomar photographer William Miller, who shines a bright light through it for a color test. If it checks out, he will know that star shots with the same film are accurate.

THE SUN'S STORY is told in a strip of photographs which make up one complete spectrum over 40 feet long. Each picture, here being studied by solar expert Robert S. Richardson, covers a portion of the spectrum, spread wide to show minute detail.

The Marvelous Secret of the Spectrum

Among essential tools of astronomical research are the techniques for deciphering light itself. As early as 1666, Isaac Newton had found that a beam of white sunlight will fan out into all the colors of the rainbow after passing through a triangular prism of glass, but the secrets locked in the colors eluded physicists for two centuries.

This puzzling phenomenon appeared even more complex when a German optical expert, Joseph von Fraunhofer, discovered, in 1814, that the sun's spectrum—as sunlight's rainbow is now called—is slashed by numerous black lines (*left*). These lines remained a mystery until 1859, when laboratory experiments by Gustav Kirchhoff revealed that the features of any spectrum are governed by the density, chemical make-up and temperature of the light's source (*opposite*). For the first time, stars were no longer pin points of inscrutable light but objects with individual personalities.

The steady progress of atomic theories made it possible to turn these mysterious patterns of light and dark into revealing messages about the physical nature and the composition of sun and stars. With the increasing efficiency of light-splitting instruments, the science of spectroscopy became an indispensable branch of astronomy. On its findings are based all the modern theories about the universe.

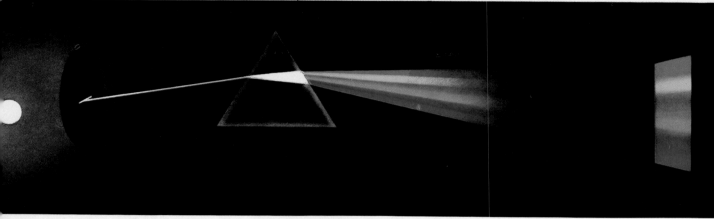

A CONTINUOUS SPECTRUM, showing the familiar hues of the rainbow stretched out in a band of blending colors, is produced by a glowing solid or liquid, or by a hot, dense gas under high pressure. White light emanating from the tightly packed gases in the main body of the sun and stars is spread into a continuous spectrum when it is focused and made to pass through a prism.

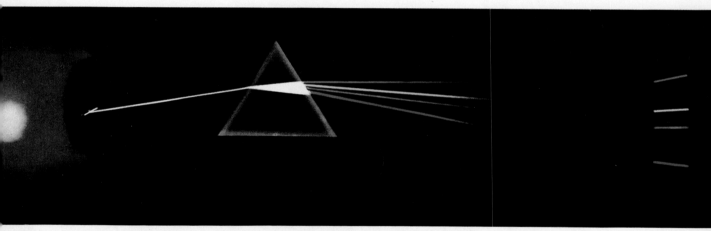

A BRIGHT-LINE SPECTRUM, or emission spectrum, is produced only by a hot gas of low density. Incandescent gas in a terrestrial laboratory or in interstellar space shows a spectrum broken into narrow, bright lines. Each chemical substance gives off a characteristic pattern of lines that differs from all others and may serve to identify that substance like a set of fingerprints.

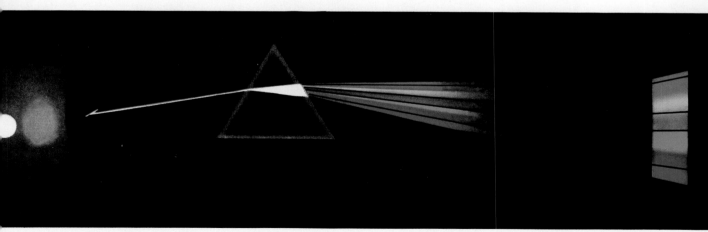

A DARK-LINE SPECTRUM, or absorption spectrum, is caused by the presence of a cooler gas in front of a source producing a continuous spectrum. The cooler gas soaks up light precisely in the parts of the spectrum where it would emit bright lines if it were hot enough. The resulting gaps in the continuous rainbow may thus be used to determine the composition of the gas.

47

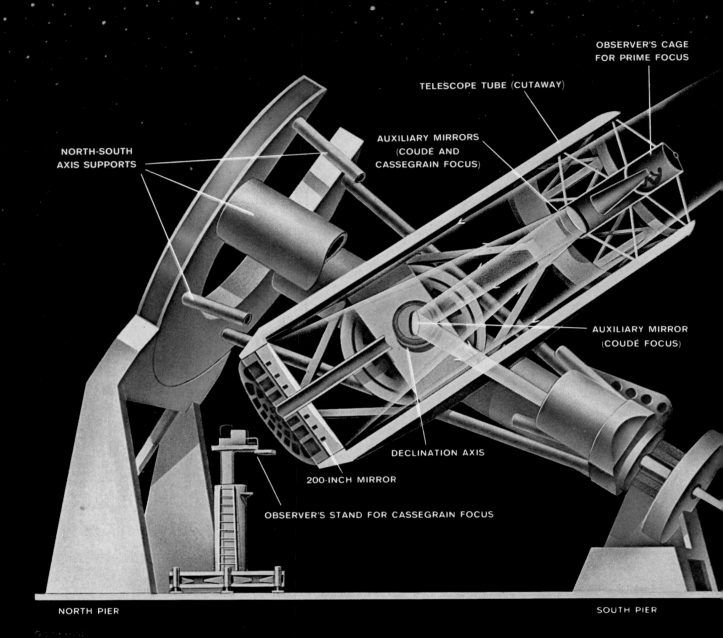

NORTH-SOUTH
AXIS SUPPORTS

TELESCOPE TUBE (CUTAWAY)

OBSERVER'S CAGE
FOR PRIME FOCUS

AUXILIARY MIRRORS
(COUDÉ AND
CASSEGRAIN FOCUS)

AUXILIARY MIRROR
(COUDÉ FOCUS)

DECLINATION AXIS

200-INCH MIRROR

OBSERVER'S STAND FOR CASSEGRAIN FOCUS

NORTH PIER

SOUTH PIER

Knowledge on a Beam of Starlight

How the world's largest telescope collects the light of a star for spectroscopic analysis is shown in this cutaway view. In essence, as much light as possible is collected by the main mirror at the base of the telescope, focused into a bright beam and then guided into a special room filled with instruments for spectrum studies. This room is maintained at constant temperature so that the by-now greatly concentrated beam of light will not be distorted in the slightest by expansion or contraction of the instruments. In this drawing, the telescope is aimed at Sirius, the brightest star in the sky. At the lower right is projected a portion of Sirius' spectrum, showing the pattern of dark lines

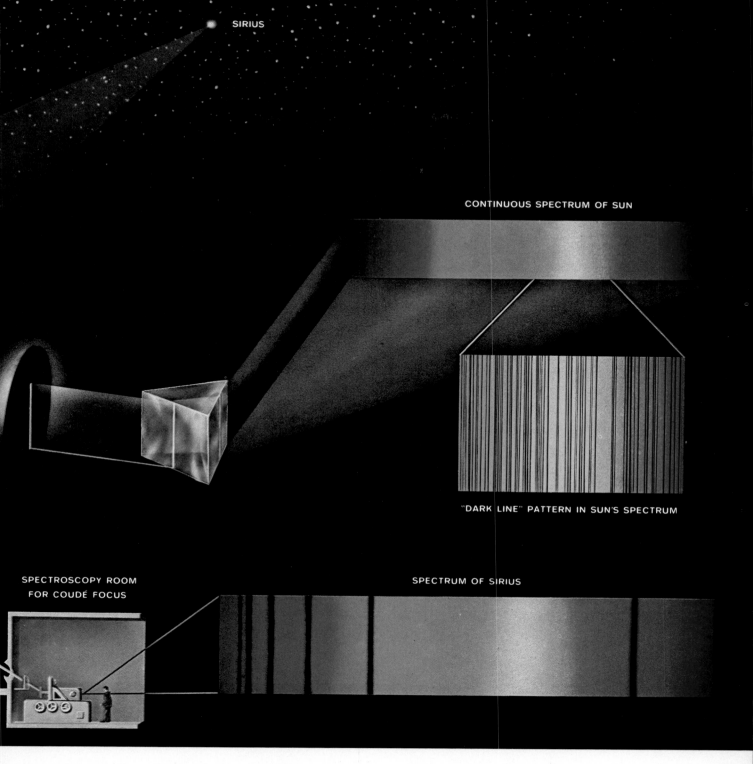

SIRIUS

CONTINUOUS SPECTRUM OF SUN

"DARK LINE" PATTERN IN SUN'S SPECTRUM

SPECTROSCOPY ROOM
FOR COUDÉ FOCUS

SPECTRUM OF SIRIUS

whose positions identify the spectral type of that particular star.

Above the spectrum of Sirius is an enlarged view of a slit-and-prism combination stretching a spectrum of sunlight. The further enlargement shows a portion of the spectrum as revealed by special spectrographs designed for solar studies.

For direct observation of stars and other sky objects, the telescope is uncoupled from the spectroscopic equipment and may then be used with one of several mirror combinations. In the prime-focus arrangement only the main mirror is used. Light is concentrated toward the upper end of the instrument to form an image of the star field. The latter is permanently recorded on a photographic plate. This requires that the observer ride in a cage inside the telescope itself. An alternate arrangement, called Cassegrain, uses a small convex mirror to reflect the light beam back through a hole in the main mirror to an observer and photographic plate at the base of the instrument.

Thus astronomy's basic tools—the telescope, photographic plate and spectrograph—combine to form a single instrument to decipher the story of starlight. The basic design of the world's most powerful telescope, the 200-inch Palomar reflector, served as the model for this painting. But the working principles illustrated here are applicable to similar equipment everywhere.

49

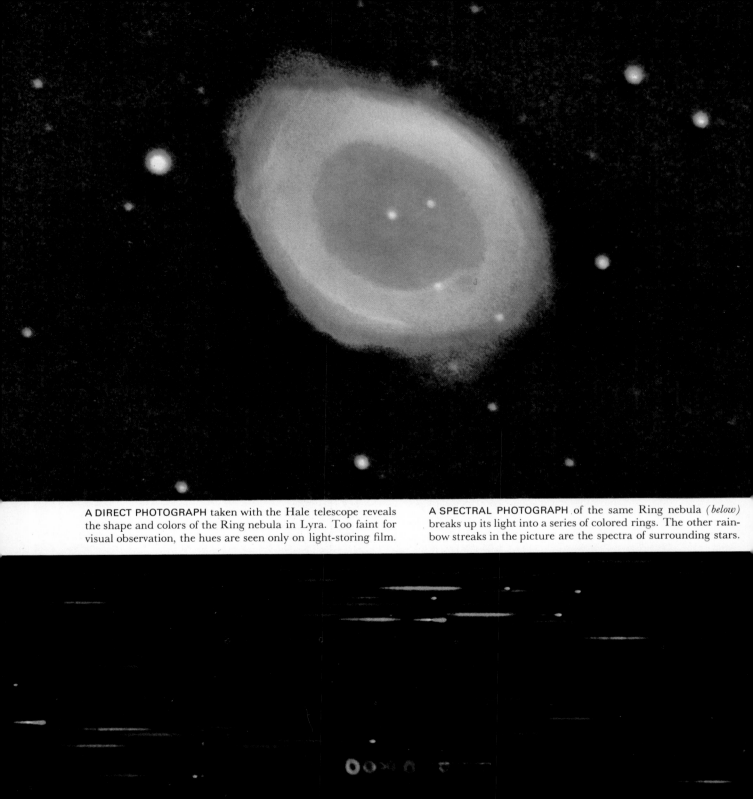

A DIRECT PHOTOGRAPH taken with the Hale telescope reveals the shape and colors of the Ring nebula in Lyra. Too faint for visual observation, the hues are seen only on light-storing film.

A SPECTRAL PHOTOGRAPH of the same Ring nebula *(below)* breaks up its light into a series of colored rings. The other rainbow streaks in the picture are the spectra of surrounding stars.

Fingerprinting the Stars

Although astronomers had long thought that the stars emit colored light, they had no visual proof because the colors are far too faint to register on the human eye. Not until sensitive, high-speed color film came along were they able to capture, in photographs, images of the heavens in their true radiance.

When the telescope is used as a huge but otherwise conventional camera, the light-storing emulsion of film can build up the otherwise invisible colors of a distant star to produce a direct portrait like that of the Ring nebula on the opposite page *(top)*. When a lens-shaped prism *(right)* is placed over the front, or objective, end of a telescope, each star is seen as a colorful spectrum which is a fingerprint of its individual personality *(opposite, below)*.

The advantage of an objective prism photograph is that it brings the spectra of several hundred stars together at once. The spectra are necessarily small but reveal enough essential features to permit quick, wholesale classification. For detailed analysis of a particular star, however, more elaborate spectra of the slit-and-prism variety are required. In them an almost infinite amount of information is available. But, in one of the ironies of science, the astronomer sees the spectra not as brilliant rainbows but as black and white patterns like those shown below.

AN OBJECTIVE PRISM, here being fitted to a telescope by astronomer Jason J. Nassau, splits the images on a direct photograph into their spectra, as shown on the opposite page.

THE COMPOSITION of a star is found by identifying the patterns of lines that its chemical elements cast across its spectrum *(right)*. Depending on an element's atomic structure, its pattern may have many lines or a few. But for any specific element the pattern, and its position on the spectrum, is always the same and unlike that of any other. By determining the exact position of a line, therefore, the element it represents is revealed.

THE TEMPERATURE of a star is indicated by the number of lines in its spectrum, as shown in the two examples at the right. The top spectrum is that of the star Vega which has a surface temperature of 20,000° F. It has few lines because at this temperature few elements can exist in their natural state. The lower spectrum is that of the star Arcturus. With its surface temperature of only 7,000° F., many more elements show up.

THE SPEED of a star moving toward or away from the earth is indicated by a shift of its spectral lines. The shift is toward the blue, or left, end of the spectrum if the star is advancing; toward the red, or right, if receding. The greater the star's speed, the more its lines shift. The amount of shift is gauged by calibrating the lines against those of a laboratory specimen, as shown at right. The top spectrum, its lines shifted toward the left, is that of a star approaching at 55 miles per second. The center spectrum, its lines close to normal, is that of a star with little speed relative to the earth. The bottom spectrum, shifted toward the right, is that of a star receding at 75 miles per second.

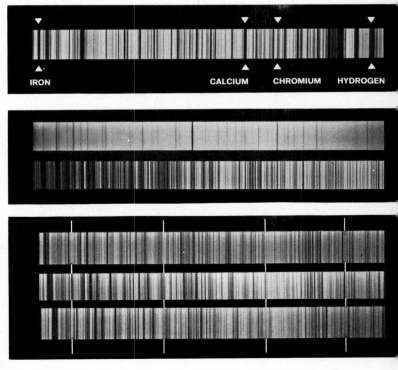

FRESH OUT OF THE OVEN after nearly a year of careful cooling, the 20-ton disk, "the world's most valuable chunk of glass," at last is ready for special packing at the Corning Glass Works.

The Biggest Eye of All

From the time of its conception in 1928 by the great astronomer George Ellery Hale, the history of the enormous 200-inch telescope of Palomar Mountain was one of drama and suspense. The casting of its mirror, twice the size of any attempted before, was in itself a costly step into the unknown. Two years and $639,000 were spent—in vain—trying to cast the disk out of quartz. Pyrex, made by the Corning Glass Works, was then chosen; but a 200-inch disk was seven times the diameter of any Corning had ever made, and the mere cooling of its solid, 42-ton bulk slowly enough to avoid flawing it would have taken nine years.

To reduce its mass, a much lighter ribbed structure was designed, which involved building a mold like a waffle iron, with cores of silica brick. Anchoring the cores turned into a nightmare struggle with heat: one disk was ruined in casting when the steel anchor bolts melted and the cores bobbed to the surface of a sea of liquid glass. Finally, in December 1934, a perfect disk was cast in seven hours of suspenseful labor, and put into a specially built oven to cool. Floods and a minor earthquake threatened it, but after 10 months it could at last be sent by special flatcar to California for the long job of polishing to the two-millionth-of-an-inch tolerance required.

THE POLISHING TOOL, a huge steel plate faced with 1,964 glass blocks covered with a special pitch, is checked by opticians of the California Institute of Technology. Including the interrup-

tion of the war, the painstaking job of polishing at Caltech's optical shop took 11 years. Over five tons of glass were removed by 30 tons of abrasives before the disk was ready for mirroring.

READY FOR COATING, its ribbed structure clearly showing, the finished glass is a thing of luminous beauty. The 40-inch hole in the mirror's center passes concentrated starlight to observers.

UP PALOMAR MOUNTAIN, the polished disk is conveyed at a walking pace under police escort in sleet and fog while anxious scientists and curious spectators form a procession behind it.

A WHIFF OF ALUMINUM, just one ounce of vaporized metal, is enough to mirror the disk's 30,000-square-inch surface. Here in the observatory shop it is being readied for a periodic recoating.

500 Tons of Precision

Mounted at last in its openwork tube and massive cradle after the mile-high journey to Palomar, the 200-inch mirror rolled back the edges of the universe over twice as far as they had stood before. Yet for all its awesome power and bulk, Hale's telescope —which its creator did not live to see—is an instrument of incredible balance and precision. One hand can turn it on its oil-pad bearings. Over successive nights, the time required for very long exposures, its computer-governed mechanism enables the 200-inch to track so faithfully that the light from stars millions of light-years away registers on astronomers' film with the sharpness of a needle's point.

OPENWORK TUBE, 55 feet long and weighing 125 tons, stands ready in its 300-ton yoke to receive the mirror. The tube and dome can move so that the telescope may cover the entire sky.

THE SPIRAL GALAXY M 81 AS SEEN WITH A SCHMIDT TELESCOPE WHIRLS AMID A VAST STELLAR COMPANY   WHEN THE HALE TELESCOPE ZE

FOR WIDE OBSERVATION, the 48-inch Schmidt telescope at Palomar is used as a wide-angle camera that has already furnished astronomers with a celestial map on nearly 1,000 plates.

Telescopes for Every Task

Big telescopes like the 200-inch Hale at Palomar can range far and deep but they have one built-in disadvantage: their field of vision is extremely narrow. Thus, while they serve magnificently to examine a single nebula in close detail, to map the heavens with them would be the work of several lifetimes. But just at the time when the 200-inch telescope was being planned, astronomers were given a perfect partner for the long-range reflectors. In Germany, in the 1930s, Bernhard Schmidt of Hamburg perfected an entirely new type of telescope based on the principle of having a large, thin lens counteract the distortions of a wide-seeing, spherical mirror.

The result of this combination was an instrument with a breadth of vision never before considered possible: a Schmidt telescope can take in hundreds of times the area of sky seen in a conventional reflector, and its images, unlike those of previous wide-angle telescopes, are sharp right to the edges of its picture. When a 48-inch Schmidt telescope—the largest of its kind—was installed at Palomar in 1948, astronomers had a tool with which they could survey vast sections of the sky (*left, above*), leaving the Hale and other long-range telescopes free to zero in for detailed study (*center, above*). The partnership makes Palomar the finest optical observatory in the world.

ON M 81, ITS CLOSE-UP PHOTOGRAPH DISPLAYS FAR GREATER DEFINITION AND DETAIL

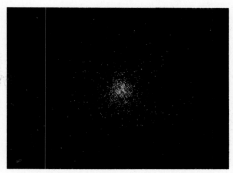

A SIX-MINUTE EXPOSURE SHOWS FEW STARS

IN 15 MINUTES THE CLUSTER IS LARGER

AFTER 37 MINUTES FAINTER STARS APPEAR

IN 94 MINUTES THOUSANDS OF STARS SHOW

FOR DEEP PENETRATION, the 200-inch Hale, precisely aimed from this control panel according to instructions from the observer, acts as a perfect partner to the Schmidt's broad vision.

STORING UP LIGHT in a prolonged exposure, the film of a camera attached to Mount Wilson's 100-inch registers, minute by minute, more and more of the dim luminosity shed by a globular cluster in Hercules, achieving a feat far beyond the capability of the human eye.

57

FIXED ANTENNA FIELD at the Mullard Radio Observatory of Cambridge in England extends for half a mile directly from east to west and covers two acres of ground. Used in conjunction with a mobile antenna which is moved on a north-south line, this system becomes an interferometer and is particularly useful for determining the position of an individual radio source.

SIGNALS FROM SPACE are studied at the Mullard Radio Observatory as they come, in the form of coded numbers, out of a digital recorder which may feed as much as a mile of tape daily.

Listening to the Stars

There are other ways of learning about the heavens than by looking at them, and scientists have recently been adding enormously to their knowledge of stars by studying them with extremely sensitive radios. That stars emitted radio waves was discovered accidentally in 1932 by a young engineer who was trying to locate the source of static in an experimental radio receiver. To his astonishment he soon realized that the static was coming from outer space. Since then, there has been a rapid development of radio astronomy, aided by the construction of huge and sophisticated antennae like those shown here.

Radio telescopes give quite a different view of the universe from the one disclosed by ordinary telescopes. For them the "brightest" star is not Sirius but an exceptionally "noisy," almost invisible shadow believed to be the ghost of a supernova in the constellation Cygnus. Why some stars emit more static than others do—in fact, why they emit any at all—is still not clearly understood by astronomers.

HELICAL ANTENNA of Ohio State University is a spiral maze on a wire mesh frame. Now used to survey distant galaxies, it was first specifically intended to record the signals of charged particles pumped into the sun's corona by solar flares. Though it is the nearest "radio star" of all, the sun gives off only weak signals except at times when flares increase their intensity.

59

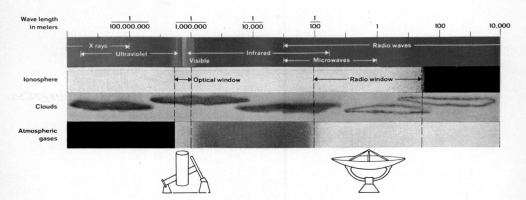

| Wave length in meters | $\frac{1}{100,000,000}$ | $\frac{1}{1,000,000}$ | $\frac{1}{10,000}$ | $\frac{1}{100}$ | 1 | 100 | 10,000 |

X rays
Ultraviolet
Visible
Infrared
Radio waves
Microwaves

Ionosphere — Optical window — Radio window

Clouds

Atmospheric gases

TWO WINDOWS allow visible light waves and radio waves to penetrate the ionosphere and atmosphere to reach the surface of the earth. Modern photographic equipment extends the optical window into the ultraviolet and infrared bands.

Through the Radio Window

Radio waves are only a small part of the enormously wide wave spectrum which includes everything from tiny gamma rays less than a ten millionth of a millimeter long to cosmic radio waves reaching lengths of 10 meters. Little of the energy pulsing through the universe reaches the earth except through the two narrow "windows" which admit visible light and radio waves, everything else being largely blocked by the atmosphere. The radio window is the wider of the two, and the view from it is curious. The sun is a pale, quiet star subject to periodic flare-ups. The planets are almost invisible, except for Jupiter. Beyond, in all directions for billions of light-years, are bodies which ordinary telescopes cannot see at all.

ENGLAND'S GIANT DISH ANTENNA built at Jodrell Bank is the world's largest steerable radio telescope. With this rig, astronomers have not only watched orbiting astronauts but have also detected objects billions of light-years away.

AUSTRALIA'S DISH ANTENNA is located in Goobang Valley and sweeps wide sections of the sky which are invisible to Northern Hemisphere astronomers. It has already tripled the number of known radio sources in the Southern Hemisphere.

3

Planets, Meteorites and Comets

ALL that man knows of cosmic law he has learned in the thin shell of life's domain, the rock-floored, air-vaulted observatory of his natural spaceship, earth. The principal proving ground for his maturing insights and theories has been—and will long remain—the nearby regions of space within the gravitational realm of the sun. Although the solar system is an absurdly small sample of the total universe, it is still 50 billion billion times as voluminous as the earth itself and it seems to include in its microcosm a surprisingly broad sample of the dynamic structures and forces of the universe at large.

Most of what man has learned about the planets other than the earth he has learned by extrapolation—a disciplined, mathematical way of using the imagination to visualize circumstances in unattainable places. Some extrapolations, however, are more dependable than others. The best of them are the ones that spring directly from measurements of masses, motions and distances. Others—involving landforms or the hues of sunsets, or how it would be to live on this planet or that—are always based on partial information and are seldom more than well-informed guesses.

The solar system is populated by one star—which we call the sun—nine plan-

SYMBOLS OF THE PLANETS

The names and symbols for most of the planets are very ancient, and the symbols are still used as shorthand by astronomers. Those for the sun and moon were probably based on old symbols for gold and silver. Mercury, the messenger, is represented by a stylized winged helmet; the gods Venus and Mars, by the traditional female and male symbols—a mirror and an arrow; the earth, by a circled cross of probable medieval origin; Jupiter, by a lightning bolt; and Saturn, probably because it was once called Kronos, by a stylized K. The symbol for Uranus, discovered in 1781, was chosen arbitrarily. Neptune, discovered in 1846, is represented by the god's trident, and Pluto, discovered in 1930, by employing the first two letters of its name.

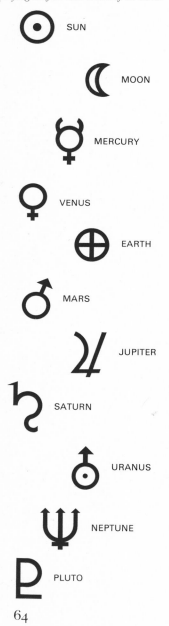

SUN

MOON

MERCURY

VENUS

EARTH

MARS

JUPITER

SATURN

URANUS

NEPTUNE

PLUTO

ets, 31 moons, some 30,000 asteroids and about 100 billion comets, plus innumerable dust specks, gas molecules and dissociated atoms. A full 99.86 per cent of the solar system's substance is tied up in the sun. Of the minuscule remainder, the earth and moon together possess less than one per cent.

The word planet comes from the Greek *planetai*, which means "wanderers" and refers to the erratic way in which the planets seem to drift among the fixed stars. Because of the rotation and revolution of the earth, the stars all seem to move in unison in regular daily and annual cycles. The planets share in this apparent motion, but they also have their own real motion around the sun and they are close enough to earth for the real motion to be noticeable. Combined with the apparent motion, this creates irregularity and confusion. Venus, for instance, takes 141 days less than the earth does to complete one revolution around the sun. In so doing, it often passes the earth on the inside lane and appears, as it pulls ahead and round the turn, to slow down, stop and then go backward.

In addition to having different speeds around the sun, most of the planets move in orbits that are differently tilted in relation to the sun's equator. Except for faint, distant Pluto, no planet orbits at a greater tilt than earth. The earth dips and rises through more than 14° of solar latitude as it gyrates Hula-Hoop fashion around the sun's waist. This means that the earth's inhabitants generally see the orbits of the other planets from slightly above or below. It also means that when the other planets pass in front of or behind the sun they seldom cross the sun's actual face but seem to circle around it, a little above or below it. Swiftly moving Mercury transits in front of the sun some 13 times each century. Venus makes two transits about every 120 years. The other planets, because they circle outside the earth's orbit, do not transit at all, but they do occasionally disappear behind the sun. If these disappearances could have been seen, the astronomers of antiquity probably would have devised a Copernican system of their own, but unfortunately the disappearances are completely hidden by the glare of the sun's light.

ONCE Copernicus and Kepler had worked out the true motions of the planets, a broad outline of the character of each planet followed inescapably. The smallest, innermost planet, Mercury, comes within 28 million miles of the sun at one end of its elliptical orbit and swings out to 43 million miles at the other end. During each revolution it rotates on its axis only once, with the queer consequence that a year on Mercury has the same 88-day length as a day. Still more unpleasant, one side of the planet is always facing out toward space and being frozen, while the other side is facing the sun and being cooked at a lead-melting 650° F. Under the circumstances, no man will probably ever visit Mercury but if, by any chance, some well-insulated astronaut should ever venture within its dangerous climes, he will not need much fuel to take off again. The mass of the planet is only one eighteenth of the earth's and the gravitational tug at its surface only three eighths of the earth's. This means that instead of having to blast off at seven miles per second—the escape velocity at the earth's surface —the visitor will need a speed of only 2.6 miles per second. It also means that Mercury's primeval gas molecules, which might otherwise have become an atmosphere, have themselves blasted off from the hot side, boosted one by one to escape velocity by the energy of the glaring sun.

The planet next closest to the sun, and closest of all to the earth, is Venus. Unlike Mercury, it is a potentially fascinating, bafflingly mysterious world. Not only does it have an atmosphere but this atmosphere is such an unbroken, impenetrable quilt of yellowish white clouds that man knows next to nothing about what is underneath. The gross features of the planet are strikingly like the earth's. Its mass is .81 earth's, its volume .88, its density .93 and its escape velocity .92. One other normally routine piece of planetary information—the length of the day—is unknown because the dazzling veil of clouds holds no marking long enough for astronomers to find the planet's equator or poles and determine its rotation period. The evidence gathered so far indicates anything from 225 days, the same period as Venus' year, to a matter of a few days.

Balloon flights with astronomical instruments over the last few years have proved that the cloudy atmosphere of Venus is mostly carbon dioxide, containing perhaps a little water but devoid of life-sustaining free oxygen. The insulating properties of such an atmosphere are so complete that astronomers have long suspected an unusually high temperature on Venus' surface. Spectral analysis of the planet's light has shown that the temperature of the cloud layer ranges as low as a frigid $-100°$ F. But recent measurements of radio waves, which probably originate at ground level, indicate that the temperature there is a flaming $600°$ F. Whatever lies below the clouds of Venus is clearly not inviting. Possibly in the distant future, if the heat-trapping clouds can somehow be disrupted, Venus might be converted into the tropic paradise of space fiction. But the meteorological know-how and sheer megaton power to do this are far more than man possesses at present.

AFTER the earth, the next planet out from the sun—and the only other planet that may support life—is Mars, 141 million miles from the sun. Although Mars is a small planet—only a tenth as massive as the earth—and although it is not nearly so fascinating as Venus, it does offer early astronauts a second possible landing place beyond the moon. Its average temperature is about 60° below zero, but man can survive this degree of cold. Its air is extremely thin because the escape velocity on Mars is only three miles per second—less than half that of earth. But the atmosphere does at least contain some water, enough to coat the polar regions with films of frost which advance and retreat with the round of the Martian seasons. A year on Mars is 687½ earth days long and the Martian day lasts a little over 24½ earth hours. The planet even has a little pallid moonlight at night, shed by two tiny satellites, Phobos and Deimos, 10 and five miles in diameter respectively.

An enduring suspicion that there may be life on Mars stems from the sight of gray-green areas that spread and shrink seasonally. In the early days of the telescope, some astronomers thought they saw long, straight lines crisscrossing the red deserts of Mars's equatorial regions. Later astronomers concluded that the lines might be canals, built by intelligent beings to help water a planet that was obviously drying up. Although the idea dies hard, most astronomers agree today that the canals do not exist and were seen by early observers only because they had pushed their eyes and equipment too far. The shifting patches of grayish green, however, are another matter. They are real and must be regions either of lowly vegetation or of gray dust being moved about by weak seasonal winds.

After the paltry pallor of Mars, the solar system seems to peter out entirely. For the next 340 million miles outward from the sun—room enough for three more sets of Mercuries, Venuses and earths—space is empty except for small, rough islands of rock and metal which altogether total less than five per cent of the moon in mass. The first of these asteroids was discovered on the first night of the 19th Century by the Italian astronomer Giuseppe Piazzi. He watched it for

41 evenings and then lost it in the twilight as it moved into the sun's area of the sky. All over Europe, astronomers searched in vain to find it again. Napoleon, while directing a battle, discussed what name to give it if it should be rediscovered. The mathematical genius Karl Friedrich Gauss—indulging his weakness for problems of astronomical arithmetic—gave up all his other work, converted himself temporarily into a calculating machine and from Piazzi's scanty observations reconstructed the lost body's orbit. When he emerged from his figuring binge a few weeks later, he told astronomers where to point their telescopes. They did and, sure enough, there was the mislaid wanderer. Piazzi christened it Ceres and later measurements have revealed it as an orbiting island of jagged rock, 480 miles in diameter and with a surface area of 700,000 square miles— equivalent to the Confederate States had they been scooped up by the roots, formed to fit a giant's fist and hurled into the heavens.

Ceres was both the first and biggest of the asteroids. Others were discovered in quick succession: Pallas, 300 miles wide, in 1802; 120-mile Juno in 1804; 240-mile Vesta in 1807. Today about 30,000 sizable asteroids are believed to exist, ranging from substantial, three-dimensional principalities like Ceres down to small flying mountains—like Icarus, which is only a mile in diameter. The number of still-smaller asteroids—the size of boulders, pebbles or sand grains— is estimated in the billions. Only some 1,600 have been watched carefully enough so that their orbits can be plotted and predictions made about their future whereabouts. Discovering them has become easy and routine. When a telescope is trained on a section of sky containing asteroids and the automatic movements of its mount adjusted to the average speed of the asteroids, these faint bodies will slowly begin to burn themselves in as luminous dots on the astronomer's photographic plate. The stars, which do not move with the telescopes, will appear as streaks of lights on the film. Ignoring streaks and plotting orbits for the dots, however, is not so easy and astronomers are usually too preoccupied with more distant matters to waste time on them.

Of the 1,600-odd asteroids that have been tracked, every one revolves around the sun in the same west-to-east direction as the earth and other planets. Since most asteroids move in a broad band situated between little Mars and enormous Jupiter, it is Jupiter which controls their motions. One effect of the big planet is a peculiar series of gaps in the thin, washer-shaped belt of their collective orbit. If an asteroid somehow sets up shop in one of these gaps, it soon begins to lap Jupiter at precisely the same one, two or three points along the celestial race track. The accumulation of gravitational yanks, as it passes Jupiter repeatedly on the same stretch, warps its orbit until it is no longer traveling in the forbidden gap.

Jupiter exercises such tyrannical power in its neighborhood that some asteroids—called the Trojans because they are named after Homeric heroes who fought in the Trojan war—are held in Jupiter's thrall much in the manner of satellites. They follow Jupiter's path around the sun precisely, five of them staying a respectful one sixth of an orbit behind and nine in front of the giant planet. Before they were discovered, France's celebrated celestial mechanician Joseph Louis Lagrange (1736-1813) proved mathematically that every planet should have, preceding it and following it in orbit, two points of gravitational equilibrium where matter could settle. Each point would be the third corner of an equilateral triangle formed by drawing lines between it and the planet and the sun. The Trojan asteroids cluster near Jupiter's Lagrangian points. Recently

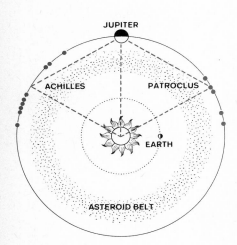

The Lagrangian points are two theoretical locations in a planet's orbit where asteroids are apt to collect. Other asteroids at other points have long since been eased out of orbit by gravitational attraction from other planets. But at the Lagrangian points gravitational stability is achieved.

The points are located by drawing two equilateral triangles side by side, with the common side drawn from the sun to the planet. The Lagrangian points are where the triangles touch the orbit, both in front of and behind the planet. As shown above, the asteroid groups Achilles and Patroclus have found relative stability in the two points of Jupiter's long solar orbit.

a Polish astronomer, K. Kordylewski of Cracow Observatory, reported that the rear Lagrangian point on the moon's orbit contains faint clouds of matter that represent a sort of second, shadow moon for the earth.

Jupiter's predominant pull on the asteroids sometimes sends one of them on a series of orbital voyages down toward the sun or up toward the outer planets. Icarus' present orbit takes it twice as close to the sun as Mercury. Hidalgo's whirls it out as far as Saturn. Eventually asteroids that stray sunward or space-ward this way are likely to cross orbits with Jupiter again and get hurled either into a new errantry or back into Jupiter's fold. In the meanwhile, they are often established on courses which bring them uncomfortably close to earth. Eros—a cigar-shaped rock 15 miles long and five miles wide which tumbles end over end as it circles the sun—can come within a scant 14 million miles of the earth. Amor, Icarus, Apollo and Adonis can pass even closer. In 1937 Hermes came so close that, to astronomers who tried to follow it, it was like the fly-by of a jet. Its closest distance was 500,000 miles—only twice as much as the moon's.

Asteroids sometimes come close enough to the earth to collide with it. Of the boulder-sized ones, which are called meteorites, about 1,500 strike each year. Full-fledged flying mountains are thought to strike much less frequently, per-haps once every 10,000 years on an average. When they do, the earth acts like so much soft mud and swallows them explosively into its surface. Geologists have only recently begun to recognize the "astroblemes," or star-wounds, which they inflict but it seems likely from the evidence unearthed so far that only the shield of the atmosphere and the healing power of vegetation, erosion and mountain-building have kept the earth from being as pock-marked as the moon.

Coming after Mars and the asteroids, Jupiter—482 million miles from the sun—is wrought on such a scale and out of such different materials that it seems like a new species. Jupiter fills a volume over 1,300 times the earth's. Its mass is more than twice that of all the other eight planets put together. It has a stupendous atmosphere, hundreds of miles deep, held by gravity 2.5 times the earth's. Instead of being a sphere of rock and metal like the four inner planets, Jupiter is composed mainly of such light substances as hydrogen, ammonia and methane—all of which are gases on the earth. Possibly Jupiter's innermost core is of rock and metal, but it may equally well be mere hydrogen, squeezed into a heavy, metallic state, three to six times as dense as water, by the overwhelm-ing weight of Jupiter's outer layers—a pressure equivalent to tens of millions of earth atmospheres.

For all its monstrous size and mass, Jupiter has a low density—only a quarter of the earth's. And this entire, bloated sphere, this tenuous giant, whirls in a day only nine hours and 50 minutes long—a speed so great that its equator bulges perceptibly and its polar axis is shrunk to only $^{15}/_{16}$ths of its equa-torial diameter. In spite of its hectic spinning, Jupiter with its retinue of 12 satel-lites—two of them bigger than the earth's moon—revolves around the sun at a leisurely 8.1 miles per second, so that one Jovian year is 11.9 earth years in length.

The atmospheric turbulence—cyclone and anticyclone—caused by Jupiter's speed of rotation is immense. Streaks of colored gases trace visible lines across the planet's face. A huge red spot, bigger around than the earth, has hovered for at least a century just south of Jupiter's equator. There is great argument over what the red spot is, but it seems to be a sort of internal moon—an island of solid stuff riding on a cold sea of liquefied or nearly liquefied gases. Another feature of the planet's stormy outer layers is a set of violently radiant belts around its equator—newly understood in terms of the earth's own Van Allen belt—which pour forth short-wave radio signals energetic enough to reach the earth some 400 million miles away.

E VEN more extreme than Jupiter is Saturn, an immense, gaseous, half-formed world 95 times as massive as the earth but only seven tenths as dense as water. Saturn revolves around the sun once every 29.5 earth years at a distance—almost double Jupiter's—of 888 million miles. It spins its light materials fast, in a day of just 10 hours and 14 minutes. Its bulging equator is girdled by three rings of snow and grit, extending from 6,000 to 48,000 miles above its surface in a washer-shaped disk that is only 10 miles thick. Beyond the rings—which are thought to constitute a sort of stillborn moon—Saturn also has nine conventional satellites. The largest, Titan, is as big as Mercury, as orange as Mars, and the only satellite of any planet known to have an atmosphere, albeit a cold, poisonous one full of methane. Saturn's five inner satellites are also intriguing: at least two of them appear to be smooth spheres of pure ice. Of the satellites that lie beyond Titan, the outermost—Phoebe—is one of the six in the entire solar system that revolve in a direction opposite to the rotation of their pivotal planets.

Saturn is the last of the five planets known from ancient times and visible to the naked eye. Nine hundred million miles beyond it, at twice Saturn's distance from the sun, lies the chill methane world of Uranus, which William Herschel identified as a planet in 1781, to the astonishment of the world. Uranus is 14½ times as massive as the earth, its temperature is at least 270° below zero, its year is 84 earth years long, and its dreary days are 10 hours and 49 minutes short. The most surprising thing about living on Uranus, if one could ever do such a thing, would be its seasons. Uranus' equator is tilted 98° out of the plane of its orbit—as compared to only 23½° for earth and similarly small or smaller angles for most of the other planets. This means that, at one end of its orbit, Uranus' south polar regions receive whatever warmth the distant sun provides and at the other end, 42 years later, the north pole is similarly blessed. Near the dark pole, daily rotation brings no succession of dawn and dusk but only a constant parade of stars circling in the night sky. During the planet's half-century-long nights it might be some solace that there are as many as five satellites in the sky at once, racing along the horizon with startling rapidity.

Neptune, the planet beyond Uranus, nearly 2.8 *billion* miles from the sun, was discovered as a direct result of Isaac Newton's celestial mechanics. Within 60 years of Uranus' discovery, astronomers had found intolerable irregularities in that planet's orbit—a deviation of almost two minutes of arc—which made them conclude that there must be an unseen planet beyond causing the disturbance. In the 1840s the English mathematician John Couch Adams and the French mathematician Jean Joseph Leverrier independently calculated where the perturbing planet should lie. Working with Leverrier's figures, a German astronomer in 1846 pointed a telescope in the suggested direction and found Neptune within half an hour. It turned out to be a pale green orb, shining no brighter than an eighth-magnitude star and orbiting around the sun once every 166 years. Two satellites travel with Neptune, one of which—named Triton—has the distinction of being both bigger and closer than the earth's moon.

Pluto, the ninth planet, was also discovered as the result of prediction. But what the discoverer, Clyde Tombaugh, found in 1930, was so much smaller than expected that the prediction may have been incorrect and the discovery an

Saturn's ring system is composed of three wide bands of minute ice-coated particles. The bands range from 10,000 to 16,000 miles in width and are believed to be about 10 miles thick. Observed from the changing positions of earth, Saturn seems to change its tilt at various times during its long 29.5-year orbit around the sun.

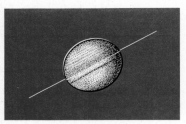

In 1951 Saturn's bands were seen edge on from the earth, appeared to form a single dark band across the planet's center.

By 1960 Saturn, as seen from the earth, appeared to be considerably tipped. All three rings and gaps between were visible.

By 1967 Saturn will appear almost edge on again, in relation to the earth. Its rings will be barely seen at the planet's sides.

accident. Pluto is a tiny sphere, apparently little larger than Mercury, and so distant as to be some 600 times fainter than Neptune. It orbits eccentrically between 4.6 and 2.7 billion miles from the sun. Its year is 248 earth years, its temperature is around −370° F. and it has no satellites. Because of Pluto's erratic orbit, which swings inside Neptune's, bringing it as much as 35 million miles closer to the sun than Neptune, many astronomers consider Pluto a former satellite which Neptune lost in the early days of the solar system. The theory is that when the sun first came alight it drove quantities of gas from nascent Neptune's atmosphere, decreasing the mass and gravity of the planet so much that Pluto drifted apart from its parent. A second Neptunian satellite, Triton, also escaped but was later brought back into the fold by chance encounters that put it into a retrograde orbit opposite to the direction of Neptune's own rotation. Pluto was lost more permanently—though there is still a chance that it may someday be recaptured.

In the frigid fringes of the solar system beyond Pluto there may be still more undiscovered planets, but an extensive search—which should have turned up anything Pluto's size out to about twice Pluto's distance—has revealed nothing. In theory, the sun holds gravitational sway out to a distance a thousand times farther than the orbit of Pluto before its influence begins to be canceled by the attraction of other stars. But any planets that may exist at these enormous distances are not likely to be big or even firm.

THE only celestial bodies known to roam the icy edges of the solar system are the 100 billion-odd comets. They orbit not only in the flat disk of the planets but also in a spherical halo surrounding the solar system and reaching out 10 trillion miles or more toward the backyards of the sun's neighboring stars. Relatively few comets have ever visited the hot central regions around the sun where astronomers can study them. Those that have reveal the astonishing fact that a comet is merely an accumulation of frozen gases and grit, no more than a few miles in diameter, with a density much less than that of water. Off by itself in space, a comet has no tail. But when it approaches the sun, solar energy vaporizes its outer layers to form a swollen head and then drives some of this material away to form a tail of incandescence pointing out toward space. The whole volume of a comet may now occupy a space larger than the sun, but comets are such bucketfuls of nothing that they weigh not even a millionth of a billionth as much. Still closer, streams of solar particles disrupt the comet further, creating explosive pockets of gas in its spongy substance and stretching its tail out even more. The Great Comet of 1843 had a tail that streamed out more than 500 million miles. Halley's comet, returning to visibility every 76 years, is so brilliant that it has been recorded in the annals of the Chinese and Japanese every time but one since 240 B.C.

Edmund Halley (1656-1742) was the first to state that comets are members of the solar system, traveling in elliptical orbits. Most of them are probably original members of the sun's family which have orbited from time immemorial. What causes one of them to leave its cold, chaotic realm and penetrate the heart of the solar system is most likely the influence of passing stars. Once in among the planets, the comet may simply pass unscathed and rocket back into its own regions to return again only when the term of its several-million-year-long "year" is up. Or the influence of a major planet may kick it into an orbit that brings it repeatedly close to the sun.

The fate of comets that play too often with the sun's fire is illustrated by the

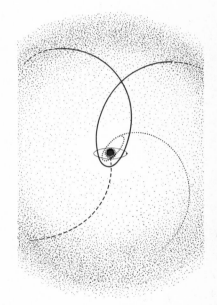

A hundred billion comets constantly circle the sun like a halo at distances of at least 12 billion miles. Most of them remain in the halo, but occasionally one is "kicked" out of its track by the gravitational attraction of a star or planet. When this happens, a comet can do any one of three things. It can be wrenched into a new small orbit like Halley's comet (dotted line), which whizzes through the solar system once every 75 or 76 years. It can make one big loop around the sun (solid line) and return to the halo. Or it can be dragged so deep within the solar system (dashed line) that it soon disintegrates.

short and wild career of Biela's comet. It was first noticed hurtling in from space in 1772. After cutting its first close caper with the sun, it began reappearing in the sun's vicinity at regular six-and-a-half-year intervals. On its swing of 1846, it abruptly became two comets moving side by side. It put in one more appearance in its split form in 1852 and then vanished. Astronomers were still looking for it 20 years later when the whole of Europe was suddenly treated to a pyrotechnic shower of meteors burning up as they entered the earth's atmosphere. The rain of cosmic sparks increased as it moved west. By the time it reached England, people could see a hundred blazing meteors a minute. Over the Atlantic, the display gradually diminished so that New Yorkers, at midnight, saw only a luminous drizzle. Careful calculations have since proved that the meteors were really the remnants of Biela's comet crossing the earth's orbit just in time to meet the earth. All the years before, when Biela's comet still *was* a comet, it had been playing tag with the earth and must have come close to hitting it.

If a comet does collide with the earth before it has been eroded and broken up by the influence of the sun, it can pack a much more substantial punch than one would expect of anything so insubstantial. On June 30, 1908, a tremendous explosion rocked the inaccessible forests along the Tunguska River in Siberia. Trees were toppled like dominoes out to more than 30 miles from the blast center. People were knocked over and windowpanes blew in at a distance of 100 miles. An engineer 400 miles away brought his train to a shrill halt as the tracks of the Trans-Siberian Railway heaved and quaked before his eyes. The pressure of the blast affected barometers as far away as England. And all over northern Europe for the whole of the next week, sunsets seemed peculiarly long and beautiful because of the pall of smoke which had been shot into the upper atmosphere. What had caused the explosion long remained a mystery. At the site itself scientists could find no sizable crater and no fragments except for minute, fused pellets—apparently of terrestrial origin—embedded in the ground like so much buckshot. Finally, in 1960, a thorough investigation was conducted by the Committee on Meteorites of the Soviet Academy of Sciences. In his final report, Chairman Vassily Fesenkov announced that the explosion had definitely been caused by the head of a comet. He put its diameter at several miles and its weight at about a million tons. In other words, the whole spectacular incident had been perpetrated by only a small comet, about a millionth the weight of similar marauders seen roaming the solar system. But this midget's orbit was such that it met the earth almost head-on, instead of overtaking it from behind, so that the combined speed of the smashup was some 25 miles per second.

THE major accidents that overtake the earth along its highway in the sky are dramatic enough to steal the spotlight from enormous numbers of lesser collisions which are really more important. In addition to its infrequent encounters with comets or asteroids, or with meteorites large enough to survive the furnace of atmospheric friction, the earth smashes into about 100 million shooting stars and uncounted billions of micrometeorites every day. All of these latter are mere dust motes, chaff left over from the disintegration of comets or from the grinding up of asteroids through innumerable collisions among themselves during their eons of wandering. But, taken all together, these tiny shocks add more than two million tons of matter to the earth each year. This, if it has been going on ever since the earth was formed, amounts to a skin some 10 feet deep over the planet's whole surface. It means that much of what the farmer plows is ancient star dust, milled and mixed for millennia by the wind and rain.

PERIODIC COMETS

Periodic comets are those which have been wrenched out of original orbits, trillions of miles from the sun, and have taken on smaller orbits which lead them to make regular and predictable visits through our solar system. Short-period comets appear every 50 years or less; long-period comets take more than 50 years to reappear. Below is a table of the 20 best-known comets visible to the naked eye from earth.

COMET	PERIOD IN YEARS	DATE FIRST OBSERVED	DATE DUE
Encke	3.30	1786	1964
Honda-Mrkos-Pajdusakova	5.22	1948	1964
Tuttle-Giacobini-Kresak	5.49	1858	1967
Giacobini-Zinner	6.24	1900	1966
Pons-Winnecke	6.26	1819	1964
Perrine I	6.47	1896	1968
Schwassmann-Wachmann II	6.53	1929	1968
d'Arrest	6.70	1851	1963
Brooks II	6.72	1889	1967
Finlay	6.81	1886	1969
Borrelly	7.02	1905	1967
Faye	7.41	1843	1969
Whipple	7.41	1933	1963
Wolf I	8.43	1884	1967
Comas Sola	8.55	1927	1969
Tuttle I	13.61	1790	1967
Neujmin I	17.93	1913	1966
Westphal	61.73	1852	1975
Pons-Brooks	70.88	1812	2025
Halley	76.03	240 B.C.	1986

TINY MERCURY, MAKING ONE OF 13 TRANSITS PER CENTURY ACROSS THE SUN, IS A BLACK DOT AT UPPER LEFT. OTHER SPECKS ARE SUNSPOTS

The Family of the Sun

Ever since the first circumnavigation, the earth—once too big for the human mind to encompass—has been shrinking steadily. Having put it in its place, as only one of many satellites that orbit the sun, man's intellect now goes on to grapple with the universe. But his guide for understanding what he learns must always be his own solar system, wheeling obediently around the parent sun.

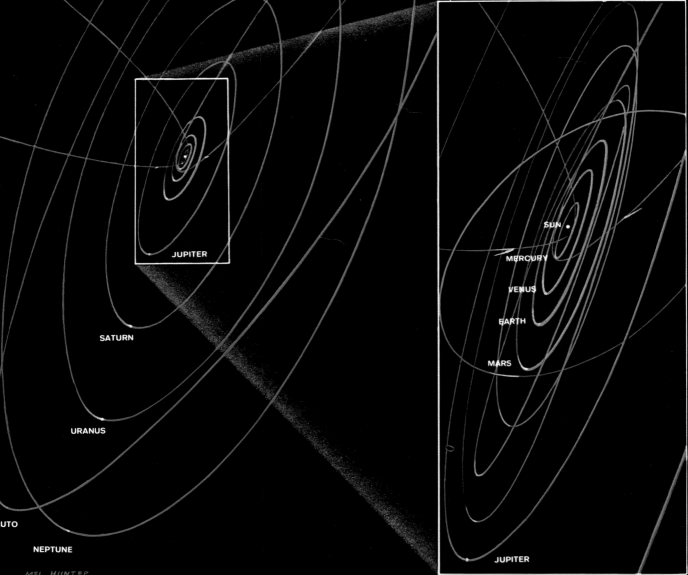

JUPITER

SATURN

URANUS

UTO

NEPTUNE

MEL HUNTER

SUN

MERCURY

VENUS

EARTH

MARS

JUPITER

Blueprint of the Solar System

One star which is our sun, nine planets and their 31 satellites, thousands of asteroids, billions of comets: these are the basic elements of the solar system. The sun, containing nearly 99.9 per cent of the substance, is the nucleus of the system and controls the movements of the planets and other bodies.

The nine planets can be divided into two groups according to size and density. First come the terrestrial, or innermost, planets—four small solid ones —including the earth. Then come the four outer giants, composed mainly of lighter elements. Tiny, distant Pluto fits neither category. The farther each planet is from the sun, the slower it travels, and the longer its year. Mercury hurtles through space at 110,000 miles an hour and takes only 88 days to circle the sun. The earth, at 67,000 miles per hour, takes a year. And outermost Pluto, poking along at 10,000 mph, needs nearly 248 years. All of the planets travel in a counterclockwise direction viewed from the north, locked in definite orbits by two opposing but balanced forces: centrifugal force which makes them want to fly out in a straight line, and the sun's gravity which pulls them into a curved path. Besides this circular movement around the sun, each planet also spins on its own axis.

Of the 31 satellites distributed in the system, most circle their planets in the same direction as the planet spins. Asteroids, mostly located in a broad belt between Mars and Jupiter, circle the sun as the planets do. Trojan asteroids are those which follow Jupiter's path. Comets, the quixotic tramps of the family, often follow immense looping orbits that take them to the outer edges of the solar system.

ORBITS OF THE NINE PLANETS and two comets are drawn to scale in the diagram opposite. All the planets circle the sun in about the same plane, except Pluto. The comets follow elliptical orbits that may carry them to the outermost fringes of the solar system and take millions of years to complete. The inset diagram shows the paths of the four inner planets, also four of the many asteroids that orbit in various planes between Mars and Jupiter.

RELATIVE SIZES of the nine planets and their 31 satellites are shown at right, with the sun beside them for comparison. Jupiter and Saturn have 21 satellites between them, the seven smaller planets only 10. But one of these 10, our moon, is exceptional. It is so much larger, in comparison with its parent planet, than any other satellite in the solar system, that it is often regarded as a planetary partner of the earth, rather than a satellite.

PLUTO

NEPTUNE

URANUS

SATURN

JUPITER

MARS

EARTH

VENUS

MERCURY

A MOUNTAIN OF ICE dominates an artist's conception of a frozen landscape on Europa, one of the four satellites of Jupiter that are large enough to be seen with binoculars. These four vary in diameter from 1,760 to greater than 3,000 miles. One of them, Ganymede, is larger than the planet Mercury. Eight smaller moons, 10 to 100 miles in diameter, also circle Jupiter.

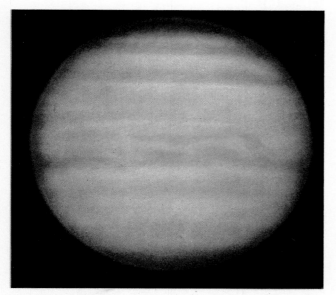

JUPITER, photographed in color, shows horizontal belts of turbulent atmosphere hundreds of miles deep. The celebrated Red Spot at upper left varies from salmon pink to greenish white.

Jupiter and Saturn, Gas Giants

With diameters of 87,000 and 72,000 miles respectively, mighty Jupiter and beautiful Saturn dwarf all other planets in the solar system. Yet each, for its size, is a lightweight. The earth's average density (water = 1) is 5.5, but that of Jupiter is only 1.34, and Saturn's is about that of a milk shake—a mere 0.68. Plunged into some Gargantuan sea, the whole planet Saturn would float.

Because of the relative lightness of these two gas giants, some astronomers conjecture that their inner cores may be hydrogen compressed into a rigid state by terrific pressure. Others believe that they have small rock cores surrounded by massive shells of ice some 20,000 miles in thickness. We know that Jupiter and Saturn have dense, poisonous atmospheres of hydrogen, ammonia and methane. These gases swirl about the planets in turbulent cloud bands

MIMAS, innermost of Saturn's satellites, could serve as a space station from which to observe the huge planet, only 115,000 miles away. The shadow on Saturn's surface is cast by its rings —here seen edge on. Only some 10 miles thick, the rings make a band 42,000 miles wide. The small shadow below the rings is cast by another satellite. Nine satellites in all circle Saturn.

many hundreds of miles deep. The two big planets have other points in common. Both of them spin rapidly, and thus have bulging waists and flattened poles because of centrifugal force. Both are believed to have frigid surface temperatures of −200° F. or lower. Both have atmospheric belts that travel at different speeds in different zones or latitudes. Both have large retinues of satellites—Jupiter 12 and Saturn nine. Both have one or more satellites that defy majority rule and circle the planet in a direction opposite to the planet's own rotation.

Finally, each has a distinct feature shared by no other planet. Saturn has its three rings—countless particles of ice or frost-covered gravel—that circle it at different speeds. Jupiter has its mysterious Red Spot—25,000 miles long and 8,000 across—which may be an island of helium floating on a gaseous sea.

SATURN, photographed in color, shows atmospheric belts like Jupiter's. Three rings of whirling ice or frosted gravel circle its equator. One ring, the innermost, is too thin to be seen here.

75

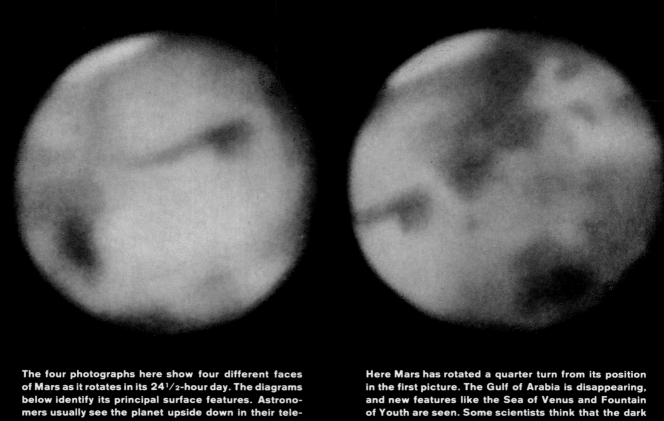

The four photographs here show four different faces of Mars as it rotates in its 24½-hour day. The diagrams below identify its principal surface features. Astronomers usually see the planet upside down in their telescopes—so the southern icecap, wafer-thin and 1,000 miles wide, appears at upper left in each picture. The dark areas, given fanciful names by their discoverers, were once mistakenly thought to be water-filled basins.

Here Mars has rotated a quarter turn from its position in the first picture. The Gulf of Arabia is disappearing, and new features like the Sea of Venus and Fountain of Youth are seen. Some scientists think that the dark areas, which change color with the seasons, may be zones of vegetation. The orange areas are thought to be vast deserts, and the muddy areas may be semideserts where vegetation is obscured by wind-swept sands.

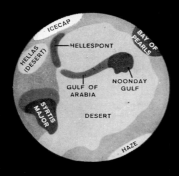

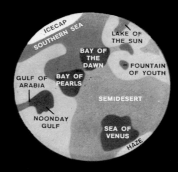

An Intriguing Neighbor Which May Harbor Life

Named for the Roman god of war, reddish-hued Mars is the only planet whose surface can be plainly seen from the earth and many of its features clearly identified. Astronomers have compiled a number of facts about Mars. They know that it has a diameter of 4,130 miles, half that of the earth. Its mass is one tenth, its gravity two fifths and its density three fourths that of our planet. Mars's atmosphere, only a tenth as dense as the earth's, contains at least twice as much carbon dioxide, but no detectable oxygen.

Clouds sail over the surface and winds sweep across the arid land. The temperature varies from highs of 70° or 80° to lows of −150° F. Some water collects as frost caps at each pole. With a polar inclination of 25°, Mars has four seasons during its 687-day year. During the long summer the frost cap recedes and dark patches appear. Experts think these are tracts of simple vegetation—something like lichens or moss. Though spectrographic studies have shown no hint of chlorophyll, they have indicated organic

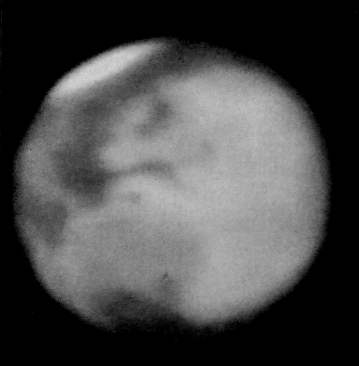

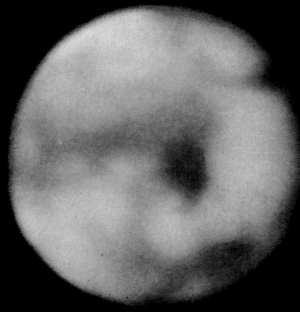

As the planet spins farther around, a vast, apparently unbroken tract of desert appears at the right, reaching close to both poles. Violent dust storms sometimes sweep over major portions of the planet, obscuring the features beneath them. Astronomers have suggested that the Martian desert may be composed of powdered rock similar to limonite or felsitic rhyolite, both commonly found in mountainous regions of the earth.

With rotation three quarters complete, the dark zone of Syrtis Major, the light-colored Hellas desert and the tip of the Gulf of Arabia again come into view. Syrtis Major, which in 1659 became the first feature discovered on Mars, is used to measure the planet's speed of rotation. The band that arches down from Syrtis Major to Utopia *(diagram, below)* is about 300 miles wide, yet some astronomers once classified this as a canal.

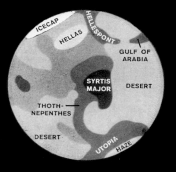

molecules—conceivably life of some sort—on Mars.

Wheeling along an elliptical orbit around the sun, Mars curves to within 36 million miles of the earth once every 15 or 17 years. Such visits—the last was in 1956 and the next will occur in August 1971—give astronomers opportunities for seeking the answers to many questions. What kind of life does exist on Mars? Just what are those dark areas? How thick are the icecaps? And what about those canals?

Ever since 1877, when Giovanni Schiaparelli,

uncle of the Paris *couturière*, reported seeing *canali* —an Italian word meaning "channels"—astronomers have argued about them. The man in the street has always preferred to debate the idea that they were built by intelligent Martian beings. So have some astronomers. In 1894 Percival Lowell founded Lowell Observatory at Flagstaff, Arizona, for the express purpose of studying Mars, its canals—and its inhabitants! Most astronomers now agree that the canals do not exist or are, at most, natural features.

WHERE LIFE MIGHT FLOURISH among planets circling a hypothetical star is a spherical zone shown in deep red in this drawing. The innermost planet is too close to the star, and too hot to sustain life. The outer two are too far away, and too cold, even though one swings into the life zone during part of its year. Only the second planet, entirely within the life zone, will support life.

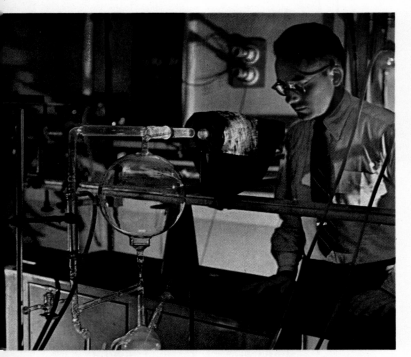

DAWN OF LIFE is produced experimentally by Dr. Stanley L. Miller. By exposing gases to ultraviolet rays or electricity, he formed amino acids, the basic units of which proteins are made.

Life on Other Planets

Living matter needs an environment like the earth's in order to evolve. First, a life-bearing planet should have a temperature range between 32° and 212° — the range in which water can exist as a liquid. At colder temperatures, chemical reactions would take place too slowly. At higher temperatures, heat would rupture the bonds between hydrogen and carbon atoms—the basic ingredients of living matter. Second, a planet must have a suitable atmosphere for living things to breathe. This means that if a planet is too small, its gravitational pull will be too weak to prevent atmospheric gases from escaping into space.

Finally, the planet's sun must be the right size. Too small a sun would generate enough heat only for a planet orbiting in a very restricted zone. Too large a sun would expand into a red giant and envelop its planets in flames almost before the processes of evolution could get under way. Despite these conditions, scientists calculate that in our Milky Way alone millions of stars may have habitable planets.

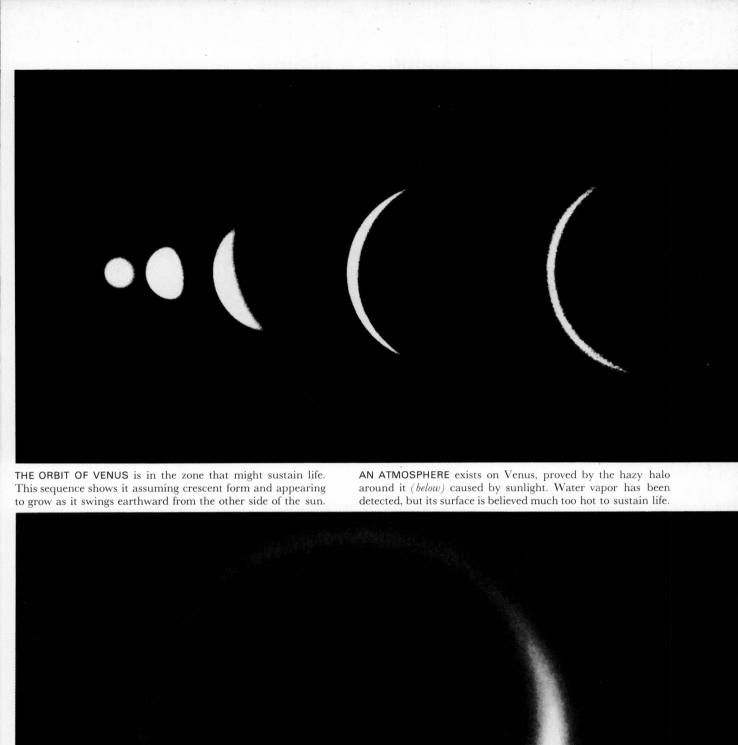

THE ORBIT OF VENUS is in the zone that might sustain life. This sequence shows it assuming crescent form and appearing to grow as it swings earthward from the other side of the sun.

AN ATMOSPHERE exists on Venus, proved by the hazy halo around it (below) caused by sunlight. Water vapor has been detected, but its surface is believed much too hot to sustain life.

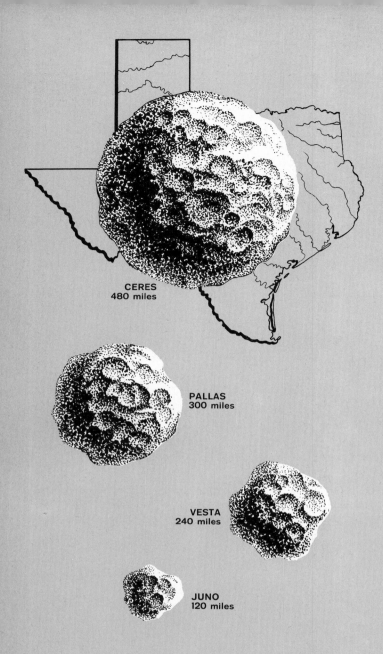

CERES
480 miles

PALLAS
300 miles

VESTA
240 miles

JUNO
120 miles

MANHATTAN

EROS

Flying end over end through space like an island torn from its moorings, Eros has about the same dimensions as Manhattan. Eros takes 21 months to orbit the sun, and closes with the earth at predictable intervals. Its uneven oblong shape was detected in 1931, when it came within 16 million miles of us. Because its distance can be fixed with a high degree of accuracy, astronomers have used Eros to refine other calculations of distance in the solar system.

WOLF METEORITE CRATER, in Australia, was discovered from the air in 1947. At least 14 such craters, or astroblemes ("star-wounds"), have been discovered on the surface of the earth.

Rubble of the Solar System

Ranging in size from specks of dust to miniature planets, a stream of asteroids orbits the sun in the broad zone between Mars and Jupiter. Altogether about 1,600 of the largest have been tracked and cataloged, but of these only about 20 have diameters in excess of 100 miles. Another 30,000 or so may be a mile or more in diameter, and millions or billions are of boulder and pebble size. Any of these that enter the earth's atmosphere are, along with the debris of comets, called meteors or shooting stars. Those that actually hit the earth's surface are called meteorites.

Although tons of tiny specks of star dust settle to earth daily, the impact of sizable meteorites (50,000 tons or more) occurs only about once every 10,000 years. Striking with tremendous force, such meteorites gouge out huge craters. The most familiar astrobleme, or "star-wound," visible on the earth's surface today is the 25,000-year-old Barringer Crater in Arizona—three quarters of a mile wide and 600 feet deep. The largest is the over-a-quarter-billion-year-old Vredefort Ring in the Transvaal, with an eroded granite dome 26 miles wide. This must have been formed by an asteroid a mile in diameter, hitting with the explosive force of a million-megaton bomb.

THE "BIG FOUR" asteroids are pictured at upper left, with Texas underlying Ceres to show comparative sizes. Only Vesta can be observed occasionally with the naked eye.

ASTEROID ICARUS, moving 20 miles a second, appears as a streak in the center of a time exposure (right). Many asteroids have been discovered by photographs such as this.

HALLEY'S COMET STREAMS A 50-MILLION-MILE TAIL, STREAKING BETWEEN SUN AND EARTH ON MAY 13, 1910. THE EARTH PASSED THROU

APPEARANCE IN 1066 of Halley's comet occurred on the eve of the Norman invasion of England. It was later embroidered into the Bayeux tapestry, which commemorates the Conquest.

Trail Blazers from Outer Space

Long considered portents of dire catastrophe, the appearance of comets blazing their fiery paths across the skies used to fill men's hearts with terror. In reality, a comet is just a dirty snowball in space—nothing but ice, frozen gases and bits of meteoric rock. Less orderly than planets, comets travel elongated orbits which can take them trillions of miles into space at one end, quite close to the sun at the other. Their periods vary from a few years to many millions. Approaching the sun, some of the frozen gases are vaporized by solar heat, expanding into enormous glowing balls with tails millions of miles long. Driven by solar energy, the tails always stream away from the sun. Famous Halley's comet has been recorded on all but one of its visits since 240 B.C.

AREND-ROLAND COMET is named for the Belgians who discovered it in 1956. The needle point is really a broad fan seen on edge. Observed only once, Arend-Roland may some day return.

THE MOREHOUSE COMET made its only known visit in 1908, changed its aspect from night to night. Several times the tail separated from the head. The flare is caused by expanding gases.

83

4

Biography
of the Sun

THE be-all and end-all of the solar system, whirlpool eye to its comets, asteroids and planets, fountain of its energy, dealer and shuffler of its changes,
producer of its principal motions, brightest light, heaviest mass and sustainer
of life—this paragon of man's cosmic neighborhood is, of course, the sun. And
though by modern understanding it has become only the frog of the solar system's pond—one medium-sized star among billions—it does remain a star—the
nearest—and as such a marvelous monster totally different from the solid planetary crags or wispy comets that hurtle around it.

Not only is the sun—with a diameter of 864,000 miles—incomparably bigger
than any planet, but it is all gas, all two billion billion billion tons of it. Even
at the center, under the crushing gravity of a million million pounds of overly-
ing matter pressing down on every square inch, its atoms still retain their gaseous ability to wander freely and to withstand the unbelievable squeeze that
is put on them. What keeps the sun's core from collapsing and solidifying is
sheer energy—stupendous floods of energy that raise the internal temperature
to as much as 25 million degrees Fahrenheit, heating not only the sun's enormous envelope of gas but the rest of the solar system as well. The source of

this energy is the conversion of matter—the slow, steady, irretrievable destruction of the sun's substance by the nuclear fusion of hydrogen atoms into helium atoms. The process is close cousin to the explosive reaction in an H-bomb, except that it is moderated and contained by the quadrillions of cubic miles of elastic gas which surround the sun's core.

At the microcosmic level, every fusion is a sequence of three kinds of collisions between atomic nuclei. The steps in the sequence do not all take place equally rapidly because the collisions do not all have the same likelihood of occurring. Some of the participants are, by their nuclear nature, far more collision-prone than others. As a matter of fact, the first collision is apt to overtake a given atomic nucleus once every seven billion years, the second once every four seconds and the third once every 400,000 years. Long as the first and last of these intervals may seem, the number of atoms in the sun is so immense that each kind of collision takes place with regularity and keeps fusion going.

In the first collision of fusion, two protons—hydrogen nuclei stripped of their single attendant electrons—merge explosively to become a nucleus of the rare hydrogen isotope, deuterium. Two fragments of leftover material, like sparks from the impact, carry away unneeded momentum and electricity. One of these —a neutrino—is a negligible particle even by subatomic standards: it has neither mass nor charge and it is so sluggish about reacting with other constituents of matter that it passes right through them and flies unscathed out of the sun and on out of the solar system as well. The other fragment—a particle of positive electrical charge known as a positron—cannot move far through the dense, tense gases that surround it without bumping into an electron, a corresponding particle with negative charge. When this happens, the two opposites proceed to annihilate each other.

The nucleus of deuterium built in this first step of the fusion reaction consists of a proton and a neutron, a combination of particles almost twice as massive as a single proton but highly reaction-prone. At its first opportunity the deuterium nucleus seizes one of the hydrogen nuclei bouncing around in its vicinity and swallows it. Out of this union an altogether new element is born, helium—not the common garden variety of helium but a rare, lightweight isotope, helium-3, with a nucleus composed of two protons and one neutron. In the smashup, a form of radiant energy is created. This radiation consists of gamma rays, the most short-wave, energetic, penetrating, destructive radiation in the entire electromagnetic spectrum.

In the third and final collision of fusion, the helium-3 nucleus regularizes itself by becoming a normal helium-4 nucleus—with two protons and two neutrons. It does this by taking on a particle of its own size and kind—another nucleus of helium-3, made in the same way as the first. Since the two helium-3 nuclei have four protons and two neutrons between them and since the final helium-4 nucleus has only two protons and two neutrons, this final union obviously means that there will be two protons left over. And so indeed there are. These surplus particles ricochet from the scene of the crash and eventually strike other bare protons, fuse into deuterium nuclei and start the whole cycle of transformations over again.

In total net effect, the three-stage fusion reaction involves six hydrogen nuclei, of which two are let go again, good as new, while the other four are converted into one normal helium nucleus, two neutrinos and gamma radiation. The resulting helium nuclei represent a kind of atomic ash which the sun's

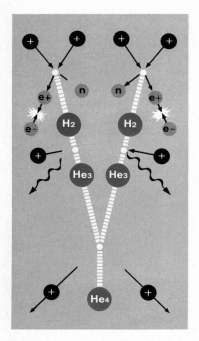

The proton-proton cycle is the nuclear process that powers the sun. It is confined to relatively cool stars, notably red giants, with central temperatures ranging between two million and 20 million degrees Fahrenheit. Hotter stars have different nuclear processes (opposite). In the proton-proton cycle, nuclei of hydrogen made unstable by heat and pressure are turned into stable helium and energy. The cycle would be fantastically slow if only a small number of atoms were involved, but there are so many of them in the sun that activity is continuous and on an enormous scale.

● *The cycle starts for any one proton when, once in seven billion years, it collides with another proton. This collision produces a deuterium nucleus, a neutrino that shoots off into space and a positron that eventually annihilates a stray electron.*

● *After a few seconds the deuterium nucleus is hit by another proton, producing a nucleus of helium-3 and a burst of gamma rays (wavy arrows).*

● *After some 400,000 years the helium-3 nucleus hits another helium-3 nucleus, producing a nucleus of inert helium and two protons. These two protons are now free to start the proton-proton cycle over again.*

KEY

+ Proton: massive positive particle

e- Electron: tiny negative particle

e+ Positron: tiny positive particle

n Neutrino: tiny uncharged particle

Nucleus: central core of an atom

fusion reactor—being only moderately hot and dense by stellar standards—cannot use again. The piercing gamma rays, in turn, are the prime source of energy for the whole solar system. The neutrino loss is symbolic of the tithe which the sun—or any other star—must pay to the empty chill of space.

The "proton-proton" fusion of hydrogen into helium that has just been described is not the only source of solar energy. Wherever there is a supply of carbon in the interior of the sun, a similar but slightly different reaction takes place. The carbon acts as a catalyst, entering into an involved set of nuclear alliances with hydrogen nuclei and emerging reborn, at the end, with a freshly minted helium nucleus in tow. Although the "carbon cycle," as it is called, is both faster and more complex than the simple proton-proton reaction, it turns out precisely the same end products: helium, neutrinos and gamma rays.

Between them, these two fusion reactions transform an inconceivable 657 million tons of solar hydrogen into 652½ million tons of helium ash each and every second. The missing four and a half million tons of mass, converted into neutrinos and gamma rays, reflect a basic nuclear fact—namely, that a helium atom is only 99.29 per cent as massive as four hydrogen atoms. The extra .71 per cent of atomic weight has to be destroyed, or the nuclear transformation cannot take place. This process of destruction obeys Einstein's famous law, $E=mc^2$. That is, the amount of energy (E) created by the process equals the mass of the destroyed matter (m) multiplied by the square of the velocity of light (c). In the easy-to-work-with units of the metric system, for example, the energy created each second—measured in watts—equals the number of kilograms of mass destroyed, multiplied by 90 million billion, which is the velocity of light in meters per second, multiplied by itself. In short, a small mass can create an enormous amount of energy.

The energy from the matter annihilated deep within the sun works its way to the sun's surface and then radiates out into space. If it did not, the solar temperature would quickly rise to such fever pitch that the sun would explode. Because we can measure the small share of sunshine that is actually intercepted by the earth, it is possible to calculate the total output of solar energy in all directions. It turns out that the sun is shining with a constant power of 380 million billion billion watts—which is equal to quite a lot of light bulbs.

From measuring this huge quantity and figuring Einstein's equation backward from energy to mass, solar physicists can deduce the amount of fuel being consumed in the sun. How they know that the consumption is being accomplished by the process of hydrogen fusion and not by uranium fission, lithium fusion or some other exotic nuclear process, is also a matter of calculation. Physicists know the sun's energy, its surface temperature, size, chemical composition and mass, and from these they can calculate the possible range of temperature and density at its core. They also know from nuclear theory and from experiments with atom smashers what the possible nuclear reactions are, as well as the temperature requirements and power output of each one. By comparing the nuclear possibilities with the solar realities, they find that none of the reactions except hydrogen fusion fills the bill. The others, like Big Bear's porridge, are all either too hot or too cold, but the H-bomb reaction, like Baby Bear's bowl, is just right. This is what physicists call a satisfying conclusion. The satisfaction comes from the fact that hydrogen constitutes over three quarters and helium nearly a fifth of the sun's mass—and of most other stars as well. Unless the primary source of solar and stellar energy involved both ele-

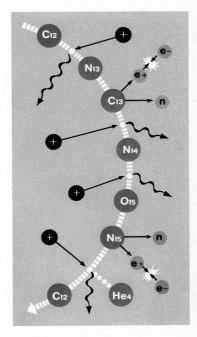

The carbon-nitrogen cycle also results in the formation of helium and the eventual death of the star in which it takes place. It occurs in hot stars with central temperatures of at least 55 million degrees F. The process requires seven million years to complete, as compared to seven billion years for the cooler proton-proton cycle.

● *After 2.5 million years a carbon nucleus (12) is hit by a proton (see key opposite), which it absorbs, changing into a nucleus of nitrogen-13, and giving off energy in the form of a gamma ray. The nitrogen-13 is unstable and quickly changes into carbon-13, releasing one neutrino, which shoots off into space, and one positron, which eventually meets a stray electron. The positron and the electron immediately destroy each other.*

● *During the next 10 minutes the new carbon-13 is struck by a proton and changes into nitrogen-14, giving off a gamma ray in the process. After four million years the nitrogen-14 is hit by another proton, changes into oxygen-15, and also releases a gamma ray. The unstable oxygen-15 becomes nitrogen-15 within a few minutes, simultaneously emitting one neutrino, which is lost in space, and one positron, which again meets an electron and ends in mutual annihilation.*

● *After about 20 years the nitrogen-15 is hit by a proton and splits into one nucleus of helium, one of carbon-12, the latter is left free to start the cycle over again.*

ments, astronomers and physicists alike would have a lot of explaining to do.

If the immense energy released at the sun's core reached the surface all in the form of gamma waves as originally created, the result would be a death ray spreading throughout the solar system. But several studies, among them the orbiting of gamma-burst counters aboard the United States satellite Explorer XI, have found relatively few such lethal waves to count in the direction of the sun. The reason is that the rays created in the core are softened on their outward journey through being handled by the octodecillion-odd atoms of gas outside the core which are part of the sun but which play no part in the central fusions. At maximum strength, a gamma-ray quantum packs several million times as much energy as a quantum of visible light. Slamming into an atom, it can sometimes break the nucleus wide open. More often, however, it spends part of its force rattling the electrons in their orbits. Then, if it hits the nucleus or knocks an electron loose, its energy is redistributed so that the gamma ray is changed into one or another of several different rays, each with less energy and longer wave length than it had originally.

An electron that is knocked all the way out of an atom from an orbit close to the atom's nucleus usually gives rise to an X ray—a kind of wave which is four to 400 billionths of an inch in length. An electron that is almost—but not quite—knocked out of an atom (hurled, say, from a close orbit to a remote one) usually gets rid of its unwanted energy in the form of ultraviolet rays—waves that are 400 billionths to about 16 millionths of an inch long. Electrons which have been jolted only a few orbits outward bring us to more familiar ground: they generally give off the sort of radiation that we know as visible light, cresting in waves from 16 to 30 millionths of an inch long. Still smaller electron jumps can produce the even longer waves of infrared, commonly known as heat, 30 millionths to 400 thousandths of an inch long. The longest waves of all—radio waves, that range from a few thousandths of an inch to thousands of miles in length—are not usually produced by dislocation of electrons, but instead are generated by large-scale movements of ionized matter. The 60-cycle-per-second pulse of electrons in an ordinary household extension cord, for instance, creates weak radio waves that are 3,100 miles long from crest to crest.

Gamma rays emerging from the heart of the sun are first transmuted into marauding X rays and ultraviolet rays. These jostle the electrons of atoms into giving off their own visible lights and warming heats. Each element's distinctive kind of atom has its own private sending and receiving wave lengths, corresponding to the pattern of its few or many orbiting electrons. When an atom is receiving energy, one of its electrons jumps the track from an inner to an outer orbit, and the energy it absorbs creates a distinctive line of darkness in the spectrum of the radiation coming up from the solar interior. When the atom is sending energy, one of its excited electrons drops back toward its accustomed orbit and thereby adds a distinctive bright line to the spectrum. Each bright emission line or dark absorption line occupies a specific position in the spectrum peculiar to the kind of atom and the electron shift involved.

Before the thermonuclear energy from the central core can cut its atom-twanging way out to the surface of the sun, it must pass through a "shell" some 80,000 miles thick where the atoms are less tightly packed and can absorb some of the impact by means of large-scale gas flows. At the bottom of this zone the solar substance not only shines—it begins to boil. Rising currents of hot gas continue right up to the visible surface of the sun—the photosphere—where they can be photographed welling up in "granules" as much as 500 miles in diameter. At the face of the photosphere, they are mostly turned back by the force of the sun's gravitational field, but bits of them spit and spatter outward, coating the photosphere with gas jets, or "spicules," which spout up about 3,000 miles before splashing down again. This region of fiery spray, known as the chromosphere because of its red color, is the sun's lower atmosphere.

The energy that has been modulated and transmitted by the outer layers of the sun is further gentled by its subsequent passage through the chromosphere. For the observer on earth, the terrestrial atmosphere is still another pacifier, and a thief as well, permitting only a portion of the whole energy spectrum to reach the battery of specialized instruments he aims sunward. Even with all these gentlings, the sun's outpouring remains so bright that it cannot be looked at directly, or photographed like a planet or a far-off star. To study the sun visually without going blind, a man needs smoked glass or other dense filters. With a telescope, he projects the image, enlarged and dimmed, on a screen.

THE qualities desirable in telescopes for observing the sun are totally different from those for observing stars or planets. With the sun, the aim is *not* to collect as much light as possible but, instead, to obtain an image as large and detailed as possible. This can be done only by special telescopes with long focal lengths. The University of Michigan has sun-watching tubes 50 and 70 feet long. Mount Wilson has another pair—60 and 150 feet long. The pride of solar astronomers, however, is a 500-foot apparatus, nearing completion on 6,875-foot Kitt Peak near Tucson, Arizona, which will project an image of the sun nearly a yard in diameter. Supported by a huge, modernistic, concrete pier, the business end of the solar telescope slants up more than 100 feet above the ground at an angle of 32° (to match the latitude of Kitt Peak and keep the instrument parallel with the earth's axis). The rest of the telescope is all underground. At the top, a flat 80-inch mirror, driven by an electric yoke, follows the sun across the sky and reflects its image down into the bowels of the telescope 500 feet away. There a second mirror, a curved 60-incher, focuses the image 300 feet back up the shaft to a third mirror that sends the sunlight into an underground observation room. From the screen in the observation room, the sun's image can be taken and dissected into all its thousands of wave lengths. By means of filters and slits, it can be photographed in the preselected light of a single wave length—and even in the wave length produced by the displacement of a single kind of electron in a single kind of atom. From spectrograms—with their bright lines of emission and dark lines of absorption—the materials of the sun's photosphere can be analyzed almost as exactly as if they were samples in an earth-bound chemist's flask.

The methods that will be refined and pushed to the limits of precision on Kitt Peak have already taught astronomers a tremendous amount about the sun's surface. Sixty-six of the 92 natural elements found on the earth have been recognized in the sun—in roughly 25,000 different states of excitement. In addition, astronomers have seen hundreds of isotopes of elements—many of them found only in laboratories on the earth—plus all sorts of strangely ionized atoms, with excesses or scarcities of electrons that would not survive for a second in the more quiet atomic surroundings of our planet.

The unstable forms of matter to be seen on the sun are simply symptoms of the general unrest there. Even the sun's rotation in space is somewhat less than orderly. Not being rigid, the great sphere's gases do not move in unison.

The rim of the equator does one lap every 25 days, while the sun's high latitudes, out near the laggard poles, take a full 35 days to complete one turn. This sort of uneven rotation, coupled with electric disturbances caused by the intense heat, keeps the sun in constant magnetic upheaval, making it a weird sort of dynamo with an ever-changing, fluid armature.

The temperature on the boisterous face of the photosphere averages 10,000° F., which, though it represents a 25-hundredfold drop from the heat at the center of the sun, is still so hot that only 18 kinds of molecules—or combinations of atoms—can hold together long enough to give off their characteristic lights and be observed. Even atoms have trouble holding together: most of them are so agitated that they remain ionized—their normal, neutral balance of electrical charges lost—most of the time. The electrons detached from them blow about freely, building up into electric winds and storms. Positively charged atomic nuclei roam almost equally free, abetted by the fact that their crowding is less than a millionth of the density of the earth's air at sea level. Because of the huge heat, the stripped atoms rush across the photosphere at enormous speed. In this rarefied zone they seldom collide, and even these occasional collisions are so violent that they capture no more electrons in their travels than they lose in smashups.

UNDER the circumstances, it is not surprising that the surface of the sun is usually pock-marked with magnetic bumps and eddies. The principal eruptions are the familiar sunspots—appearing as dark, sculptured "holes" in the bright white skin, 500 to 50,000 or more miles wide. Mysteriously waxing and waning in strength every 11 years, sunspots seem to be part of a larger, 22-year cycle in which the entire magnetic field of the sun may reverse itself, the north magnetic pole changing into a south pole and the south into a north. The last reversal took place in 1957-1958, when sunspots were at maximum intensity. At present (in 1962), the north geographical pole of the sun is magnetically a weak but strengthening south pole. Sunspot activity is nearing its minimum. The zone of activity is slowly migrating south from the upper solar latitudes toward the equator where—by 1963—the spots should no longer appear. New spots will then reappear, with the active zone again descending from the sun's upper latitudes, and reach their greatest activity in 1968 or 1969.

During their brief lives—three to four months is a maximum—most sunspots travel Indian file in pairs, one in front and one behind, as the turning sun exposes them to view. In the sun's northern hemisphere the spots that travel in front of their partners currently show north-pole polarity. The ones that trail along behind show south-pole polarity. In the sun's southern hemisphere the situation is reversed, with souths leading norths. In the late 1960s, however, when the geographic north pole has become strongly southern in its magnetism, the hemispheres will be interchanged and south-polarity sunspots will lead in the northern hemisphere while norths lead in the southern hemisphere. Sometime after 1969 the magnetism of the sun's geographical poles should begin to wane again and will probably reverse in 1979, when an entire double cycle of sunspots has gone by.

According to the theories of a brand-new branch of physics—with the forbidding name of magnetohydrodynamics—sunspots may be regions where huge, billowing hoops, following magnetic lines of force that flow inside the sun, break through the surface of the photosphere and have to complete their circuits through the tenuous solar atmosphere beyond. Presumably the hoops alternately submerge and surface, and drift to and fro between the poles, because they interact with the rotating, magnetic armature of the sun as a whole. In any case, enormous arches of extra-bright gas, like iron filings between a titanic magnet's poles, often are seen to hang high in the sun's atmosphere above the exposed north and south poles of a pair of sunspots. Sometimes these arches reach to a height of 30,000 miles and bridge a span of more than 125,000 miles—half the distance that separates the earth from the moon.

Prominences that have quietly arched across thousands of miles for days on end may abruptly explode, propelling atoms out into space at speeds even higher than the escape velocity—387 miles per second—imposed by the sun's tremendous gravitational field. Other magnetic discharges create tornadoes and leaping tongues of fiery hydrogen which shoot up 100,000 miles or more above the sun's surface. The greatest of all such spouts of ionized gas—plasma, as it is called—are the solar flares. These outbursts propel some of their particles all the way to the earth where, interacting with our upper atmosphere, they black out short-wave radio transmission and create the shimmering ribbons of the polar auroras.

The first borderland into which these gassy ghosts of the sun make their forays is the corona, the sun's outer sheath. Beyond the corona, a further, ethereal mist of matter, agitated and replenished by the solar winds which blow from prominences and flares, may very well extend invisibly and with ever-diminishing density out to the farthest frontiers of the solar system. But the corona reaches out hardly as far as Mercury, and the part of it that can actually be seen is far smaller, reaching at most one sixth of this distance. This small, visible portion can be seen during eclipses—or even in full daylight, thanks to a marvelous optical device invented in 1930 by the French astronomer Bernard Lyot. With Lyot's coronagraph, which creates an artificial eclipse by masking the main light of the sun, the corona appears as a faint, nebulous light reaching out along spokes in all directions from the sun's hidden hub.

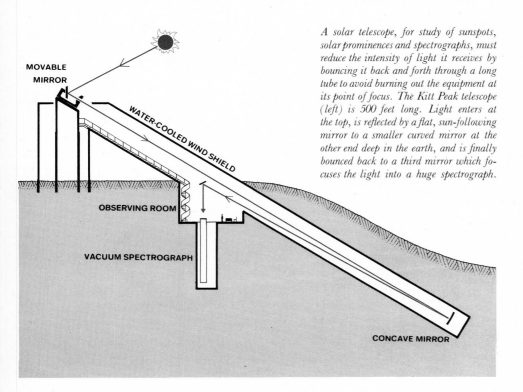

MOVABLE MIRROR

WATER-COOLED WIND SHIELD

OBSERVING ROOM

VACUUM SPECTROGRAPH

CONCAVE MIRROR

A solar telescope, for study of sunspots, solar prominences and spectrographs, must reduce the intensity of light it receives by bouncing it back and forth through a long tube to avoid burning out the equipment at its point of focus. The Kitt Peak telescope (left) is 500 feet long. Light enters at the top, is reflected by a flat, sun-following mirror to a smaller curved mirror at the other end deep in the earth, and is finally bounced back to a third mirror which focuses the light into a huge spectrograph.

The cosmic rays shot off from the sun's chromosphere and corona—like the neutrinos from the sun's central furnace and, indeed, the entire gaudy gamut of its radiation—all represent an irretrievable loss. The sun may conceivably gather in more matter—more atoms for burning—from the clouds of interstellar gas through which it wanders with its retinue of planets, but such gains are not nearly enough to replace the fuel it burns. Therefore, it is clear that from the moment the sun first began to blaze billions of years ago, it has been spending its energy and inevitably aging.

Astronomers today have a remarkably consistent idea of how the sun was born and of how it will ultimately die. The early stages have been worked out by the astronomer Gerard P. Kuiper, of the University of Arizona. In presenting his solution to the mysteries of solar creation, Kuiper modestly says, "It is not a foregone conclusion . . . that the problem has a scientific solution. For instance, an enclosure in which the air has been stirred gives, after some delay, no clue on the nature or the time of the stirring. All memory of the event within the system has been lost." Undogmatic as Kuiper is, however, his ideas have been so widely accepted and agree so well with the facts that they must represent far more of reality than error.

According to Kuiper and other astronomical detectives who helped supply clues for his theory, the sun came into being about five billion years ago—which was at least five billion years after the formation of the Milky Way Galaxy itself. The gas out of which the sun condensed was much like the gas which wanders in clouds between the stars of the Milky Way today. It was dark and full of swirls and eddies. Its substance was almost all hydrogen—but not quite all, because the pure, primordial hydrogen from which the cosmos is thought to have originated had already been contaminated by other elements created and thrown off by nuclear transformations in the earliest stars.

What made the gas of the future sun begin to condense was presumably a chance eddy that brought together enough atoms in one region so that their total gravity overcame the momentum of their individual movements and held them together in a single, collapsing cloud. Very slowly the matter of the cloud began to fall inward on eddies where the gas was densest. By far the largest of the eddies was the protosun. Its overwhelming gravitational influence shaped the rest of the cloud into a huge, rotating disk. Every additional bit of gravitational contraction worked to speed up the disk's rotation—just as a whirling ice skater quickens his spin by bringing his outstretched arms in closer to his body. Every increase in rotation speed proceeded to flatten the disk further. Within the disk the helter-skelter movements of atoms and molecules were slowly evened out by collisions, and the heat of the collisions was radiated off into space. In this way, the energy of the cloud's many internal motions was reduced and the primordial particles were reined in until they mostly whirled in orderly fashion around the protosun or around the lesser eddies in the cloud. These lesser eddies, rolling lazily around on one another like ball bearings, were the protoplanets. They, too, sorted out their internal motions and began to contract. The heavy substances in them tended to condense first and to congregate toward their centers.

In the meanwhile, the jostling crush of atoms falling into the protosun was creating heat inside it—heat that gathered more quickly than it could be shed. The temperature in the protosun's core rose steadily. As the core's temperature passed the million-degree mark, thermonuclear reactions between heavy and

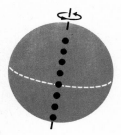

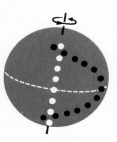

The sun's rotation on its axis, unlike the earth's, is not uniform. Inasmuch as the sun is a hot ball of gas and not a solid, it rotates faster at the equator and slower nearer the poles. The top diagram shows a straight line of theoretical dots, representing the sun about to begin rotating on its axis. The diagram below shows where these dots would be after the sun has made one revolution. The dots at the equator take only 25.33 days to make one revolution; the dots halfway to the poles take 28 days; those three quarters of the way to the poles take more than 33 days.

light hydrogen atoms began adding appreciable amounts of energy to the heat already being released by contraction. The surface of the sun turned slowly red and hot, orange and hotter, yellow and incandescent. Its first red rays, falling on the half-begotten protoplanets, began to drive away the smoke of matter in which they had been born and on which they were still feeding and growing. Soon the protoplanets were no longer rolling around on one another like ball bearings but flying as separately as bees around a newly opened flower.

As the mists of creation were dispelled and the scene gradually brightened, the innermost planets lost most of the light chemical elements from their outer gassy regions and retained mainly the heavy irons and rocks—and the liquids and gases trapped inside them—which had already formed into solid masses. Mercury and Mars, which had been condensing rather slowly out of somewhat rarefied regions in the primordial cloud, had little in the way of solid cores to hold on to, so they became small planets. The earth and Venus had done better and remained larger. In the asteroid belt the solid condensates had never had time to pull together at all and were destined to be separate lumps for all eternity. Beyond the asteroid belt where the young sun's radiation was weakened by distance, several huge accretions existed which could hold on to most of their light elements. They became Jupiter, Saturn, Uranus and Neptune, and they retained almost as large a percentage of light substances—like hydrogen, ammonia or methane—as there must have been in the primordial cloud itself.

Beyond Neptune, where the gravitational influence of the protosun had been weak, the primordial cloud had been less flattened into a disk and its motions had been less regularized. As the outflowing light of the sun drove off the gassy remnants of the cloud from these outer regions, millions of small bodies were left behind, too weak gravitationally to condense into solid spheres, but strong enough to resist being driven out of the system altogether by the push of the faint sunlight that reached them. There they remain to this day—celestial fossils pursuing their primeval orbits and revealing in their loose, snow-filled structure what the earliest condensations of the solar system must have been like. They are, of course, the comets. And as one of them approaches the sun today and grows a tail of evaporating gas pointing out to space, it gives a picture in miniature of what the protoplanets must have looked like when the young sun drove away their gassy outer envelopes.

At the sun's first dawn, several of the protoplanets had not yet ironed out all the subsidiary eddies in their spheres of influence nor finished collecting all the solid nuclei of matter which had condensed in them. At the same time that the protoplanets lost most of their gases, they also lost the gravitational power needed to finish pulling in their outriding fragments. These leftover subplanets either became permanent satellites or drifted away as independent bodies.

ONE key problem that plagues the builders of model solar systems is the fact that the sun, with over 99 per cent of all the system's matter in its possession, has a mere 2 per cent of the system's angular momentum—the property that keeps the sun rotating and keeps the planets revolving around it. The lightweight planets, in consequence, contain under one per cent of the system's matter but a staggering 98 per cent of its angular momentum. A theory of evolution that fails to account for this peculiar fact is ruled out before it starts. Kuiper has a tentative solution for this problem which, admittedly, is very speculative. During their evaporation, he suggests, the gases between the protoplanets and the sun became ionized, and in this electrical state they acted as a bridge for the

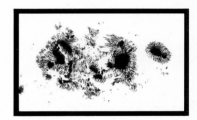

Sunspots appear to be symptoms of giant magnetic solar storms. They range in size from a few hundred to many thousands of miles across. The illustration at bottom shows that each of these spots has a nucleus, or umbra, which looks dark because at 8,400° F. it is cooler than the sun's 10,000° surface temperature. A lighter, slightly hotter penumbra edges the umbra.

Sunspots occur in groups. They make their appearance about 30° north or south of the solar equator, and travel toward it, disappearing when they get to within 8° of it. An individual sunspot is short-lived and rarely survives more than two revolutions of the sun—about 50 days. But there is some overlapping as one fades and another replaces it, creating the impression that a single group, rather than a series of groups, journeys toward the equator.

SUNSPOT POLARITY

Sunspots are like enormous magnets. Occurring in pairs, one will act as a positive pole and its companion, tagging along, will be a negative pole. This polarity will be maintained over an entire 11-year cycle, as a succession of sunspots slowly works its way toward the solar equator and disappears. But when a new set of sunspots forms in the higher latitudes, their polarity will be reversed; the leader will now be negatively charged instead of positively charged, and this reverse polarity will endure for a further 11-year cycle. Sunspot groups in the Southern Hemisphere always have a polarity opposite to that of matching Northern Hemisphere groups.

In 1940 two sunspot groups formed near 30° N. and S. The Northern Hemisphere leader was positively charged. The Southern Hemisphere's leader was negative.

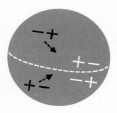

In 1950 the two groups reached the area around 8° above and below the equator and began fading as two new groups with reversed polarity began near 30° N. and S.

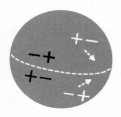

In 1960, 20 years later, the cycle began again. Two groups, similar in charge to the 1940 groups, were again seen starting out from the area around 30° N. and S.

sun's magnetic energy. In effect they acted as elastic spokes between the sun's whirling hub and its rims of evaporating protoplanets. Through the spokes the sun got rid of rotational energy and spun more slowly while the fleeing fog of the primordial cloud gained energy and spiraled outward ever more swiftly. The planets, too, increased their speeds. At the same time the tilt of their poles was increased to nearly present angles by the unbalanced force of the sun evaporating their tenuous outer substance always from one direction, off their equators.

The first light of the sun was very dim because the sun was still contracting and the thermonuclear fuel in the sun's core was cooler and less tightly packed than it is now. Once the sun stopped contracting—a culmination that took approximately 80 million years—the solar energy rose to within 20 per cent of its present value, driving off the last of the primordial cloud and leaving the planets to work out their further evolution alone. In the first 100 million years, six lost satellites like Neptune's Triton were recaptured by their parent planets in retrograde orbits. Since then, some asteroids have been swallowed by collisions with Jupiter, the earth, the moon and the other planets and satellites; some gobs of iron and rock have resettled themselves in the interiors of planets; and some trapped gases and liquids have escaped to augment the atmospheres which the planets managed to retain during the evaporation period. But by and large the solar system has probably remained much the way it was created. The sun's family, however, cannot remain unchanged forever because the prime-moving sun must itself start to change again as it consumes more and more of its supply of hydrogen fuel and begins to die.

THE future evolution of the sun has also been worked out by astronomers, notably by Martin Schwarzschild of Princeton University and Allan Sandage of Palomar. If the sun could continue to spend only 657 million tons of hydrogen each second, it would go on burning for another 50 billion years or more. But unfortunately, in a relatively short time as cosmic affairs go, rising temperature caused by the sheer weight of ash in the sun's core will ignite other nuclear processes besides fusion and the sun will start consuming its fuel at a far more prodigal pace than it does now. In about five billion years the quickening will set in and the sun will start swelling. Its photosphere will grow cooler per square mile but its over-all output of energy will grow greater. Over a span of about a billion years the average temperature on earth will rise to something like 1,000° F. and—unless some superhuman race shows extraordinary forethought and devises marvelous shielding—the oceans will boil away, lead will melt like molasses and, in the words of Palomar's Sandage, "conditions will be miserable."

Later, after terrestrial life has probably been exterminated, the sun will shrink again, perhaps undergoing instabilities and eruptions as it does so which may spray the remaining outer planets with destructive gamma rays. In its last long extremities, it will continue to shrink while the nuclear fires inside it go out and the only glow it emits is energy from the gravitational squeeze of its spent, collapsing matter. Little by little it will dwindle in size until it is smaller than the earth, its gases so densely packed that a bucketful of them will be more massive than a battleship. For hundreds of billions of years more, the sun will continue to cool off, radiating sluggishly in the infrared. Then ultimately it will go out completely, black and cold as the most remote regions of space around it. One might well ask how astronomers presume to know such things. The disquieting answer is that they know them simply by looking around at other stars and seeing what is happening to them.

THE WORLD'S FIRST HYDROGEN FUSION BLAST, AT ENIWETOK IN 1952, WAS CAUSED BY THE SAME NUCLEAR PROCESS THAT POWERS THE SUN

The Star We Live By

No other object in the universe is as important to man as the sun, the central fire upon which depend all life on the earth and any life there may be elsewhere in the solar system. Less than a century ago, no one knew how the solar furnace really worked. Now, with the principles of nuclear fusion understood, man not only knows what processes go on in the sun, but he can even duplicate them.

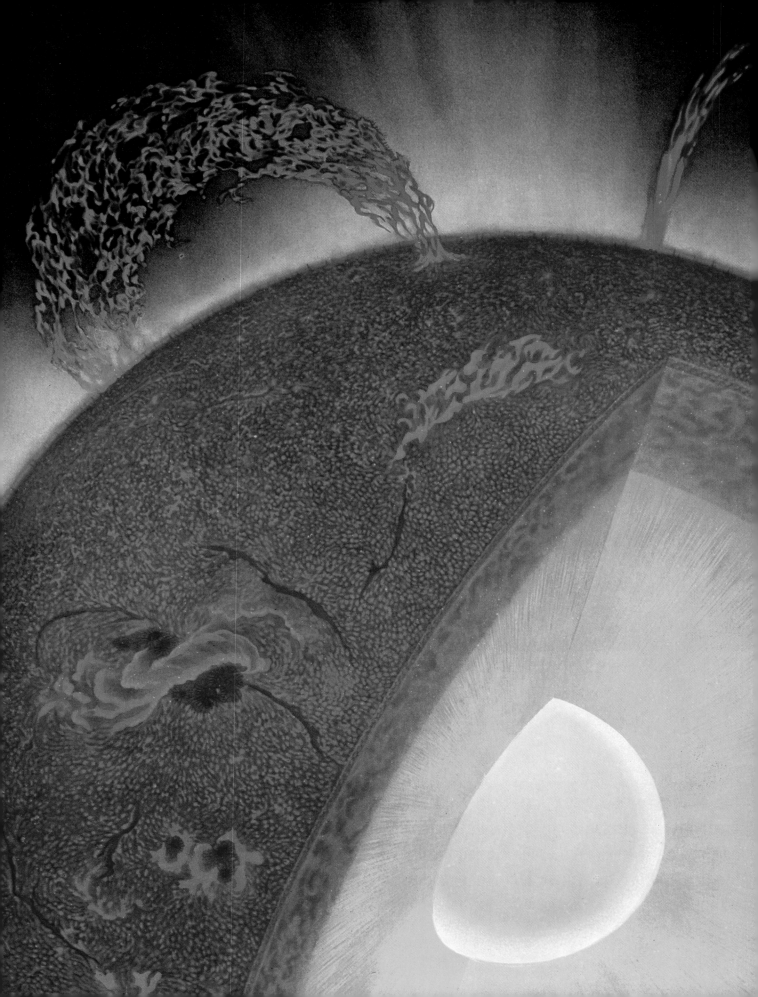

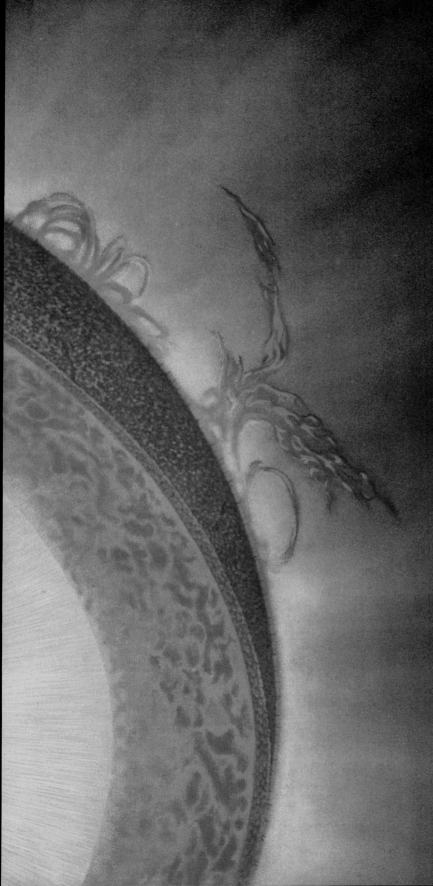

A Close Look at the Solar Furnace

The sun's vast sphere, 864,000 miles in diameter, contains 335 quadrillion cubic miles of violently hot gases that weigh more than two octillion tons. Direct study can probe no deeper than the sun's double atmosphere (the tenuous outer corona and the shallow, inner chromosphere) and its surface skin (the photosphere), because only the energy from these two zones reaches the earth after a 93-million-mile journey in the form of visible light or invisible radiation. Yet the density, temperature and composition of the gases in the sun's hidden interior have been calculated, and astrophysicists know the nuclear processes that make them burn.

The sun's core (lower left) is the heart and starting point of all its power. Here, hydrogen atoms are fused into helium at a temperature of 25 million degrees F. Energy, released in the form of violent gamma rays, pours toward the surface of the sun, 300,000 miles above.

The next part of the sun's power plant is a vast zone, shown in arbitrary size, where densely packed gas atoms undergo a savage bombardment by the gamma rays from the core. Such collisions turn the gamma rays into slower forms such as X rays and ultraviolet waves.

The photosphere, a turbulent layer thought to be 80,000 miles thick, is churned by the thrust of energy from below. Its outer boundary, the sun's surface, is marked by white-hot sunspots (far left) that appear dark in contrast to its far more brilliant 10,000° F. luminosity.

The chromosphere, a scanty 10,000 miles in depth, is the sun's dense lower atmosphere consisting largely of hydrogen. Gases, when flung up from the chromosphere, cause such displays high above the surface as the great arch and the jetlike flare shown at upper left.

The corona, the outer atmosphere of the sun, is bright enough to be observable only near the disk's edge. Beyond that it extends invisibly all the way to Mercury, 36 million miles distant from the sun—equivalent to the earth's atmosphere stretching out beyond the moon.

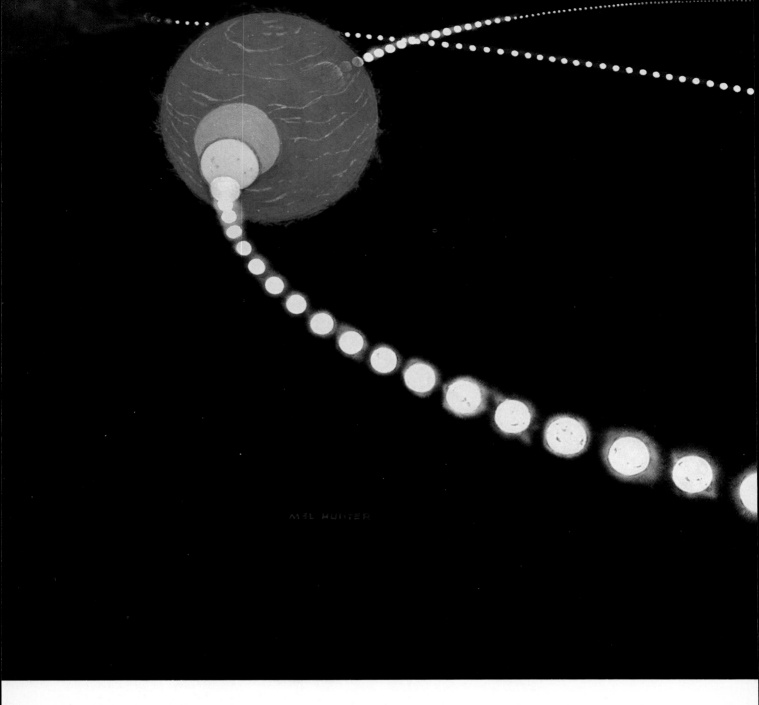

MEL HUNTER

A Journey from Cloudy Birth
to Frozen Extinction

By the enormous standards of astronomical time, the sun is a relative newcomer to its galaxy. The Milky Way is more than 10 billion years old, yet the sun is only half that. It was born (*top left*) out of a cloud of gas some five billion years ago and quite quickly assumed the characteristics it has today. Fortunately for mankind, the sun is only a middleweight star and can be expected to enjoy a long middle age before swelling to red gianthood. In this painting, which follows the sun from birth to

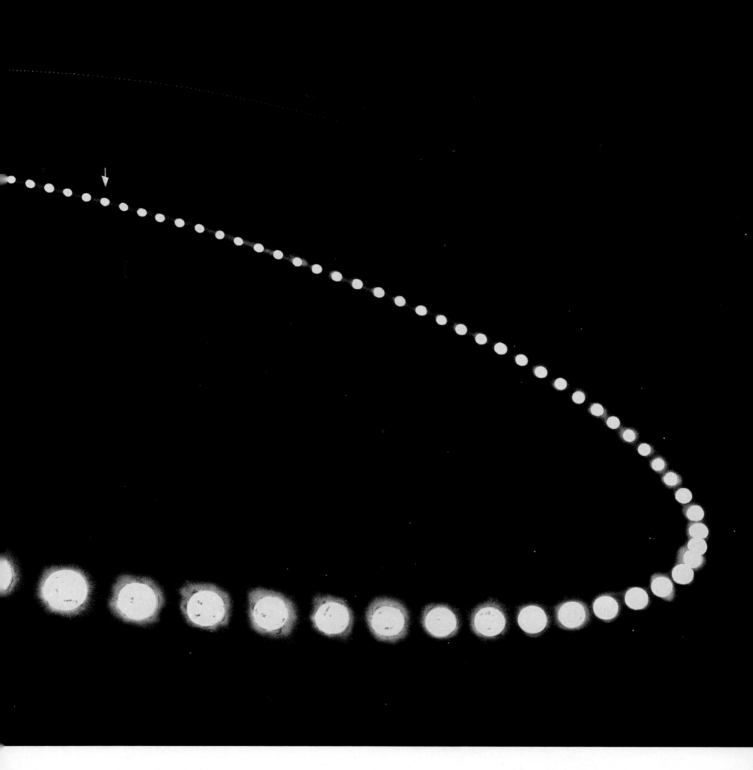

death, each spot represents the passing of some 80 million years. The arrow shows the sun's present position in time. Five billion years of normal life have passed and another five billion lie ahead. By then, however, the fusion reactions inside the sun will have deposited so much helium ash in its core that its nuclear furnace will be forced into hotter, livelier reactions. The sun will then expand enormously. This expansion will cool its surface, first to orange, then to red, but because of its increased size the total heat it will radiate will be far greater than normal. Mercury will be baked, Venus fried, and the surface temperature of the earth will rise high above the boiling point. This prodigal outpouring of heat and energy will be too great to be sustained for very long, and after some two billion years the sun will start to shrink again. In its final long decline it will fall to white dwarfdom and cool off. After 50 billion years it will have turned black, as heatless as the empty space surrounding it.

AIMED AT THE SUN, the large coronagraph at the U.S. Air Force Sacramento Peak Observatory in New Mexico artificially eclipses most of the light it receives and lets only the faint image of the solar atmosphere reach the bank of instruments that it feeds. Cameras record the brief life of solar prominences, and the corona's light is also captured for spectroscopic analysis.

Studying the Sun

Since the sun is too blinding for study with the naked eye, astronomers have learned to make special solar telescopes—systems of lenses that throw an image, magic-lantern fashion, on a screen. Images of the sun gathered in this way are large and clear and have revealed many details of the sun's surface. Sunspots have been studied exhaustively and, although their cause remains obscure, it is known that the smallest ones are the most common and last only a few hours or days; that big ones last a month or more and may cover six billion square miles; and that sunspot activity follows an 11-year cycle.

Even with the solar telescope, the sun's disk is so bright that its atmosphere cannot be seen except during a total eclipse. However, in 1930 a French astronomer, Bernard Lyot, devised a means of inserting a small black disk inside a solar telescope, thereby producing permanent total eclipses. Now, instead of studying the sun's atmosphere for two or three minutes at a time over intervals years apart, astronomers can do it at their leisure all the year round.

INSIDE VIEW of a coronagraph's tube shows the series of diaphragms that capture scattered sunlight. Because atmospheric haze worsens scatter, mountain sites are best for coronagraphs.

THE WORLD'S LARGEST solar telescope is at Kitt Peak, Arizona. The tube of a telescope must be very long for solar work, and most of this instrument is beneath the ground, running down to the left as a subterranean continuation of the slanted section visible here. The purpose of the slant is to point the instrument at the North Star; this makes daily tracking of the sun much easier.

Fireworks in the Sun's Atmosphere

The sun's surface consists of a seething mass of hot gases and sub-atomic particles with an average temperature of 10,000° F. It is rent by tremendous turbulences from below which bubble up to form sunspots and also cause the towering bursts known as prominences. These come in a variety of forms. The smallest are called spicules, last only about five minutes and rise only a few thousand miles. As many as 20,000 of them are visible at any one time. Much more dramatic are the spectacular forms called loops and arches, which may soar half a million miles or more and last for hours.

Little is known about prominences, although they are believed to be blasts of very hot gas shot upward like shock waves by pulsations from within the sun. Some can be seen as they soar high in the atmosphere; others seem to ignite aloft and flame back toward the sun. Many of them are linked with sunspots, some mysteriously are not.

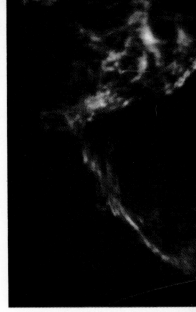

A BRIGHT PAIR of prominences, a squat burst (*right*) and a tall tongue of flame (*left*), was photographed at

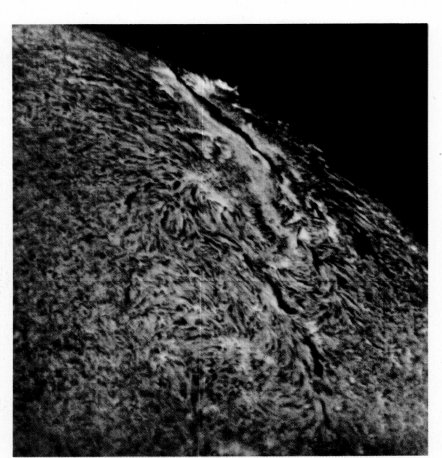

SEETHING SURFACE of the sun, photographed in hydrogen's red wave length, is seen in this plate made at Mount Wilson in 1915. The two dark, ribbonlike filaments are called flocculi and would appear as solar prominences (*right*) if viewed in profile.

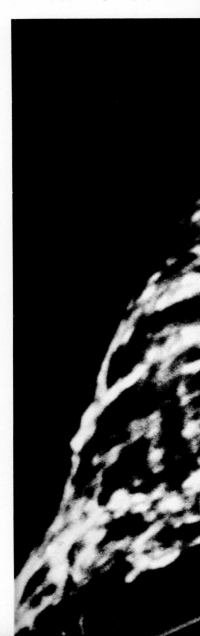

AN ERUPTIVE ARCH, one of the largest solar explosions ever recorded, was photographed (*right*) in June 1946, when about one hour old. It remained visible for more than two hours and stretched nearly a million miles into space before it disappeared.

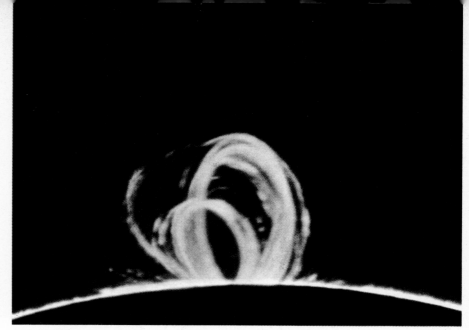

the High Altitude Observatory of the University of Colorado. The larger prominence is 250,000 miles high.

A LOOP PROMINENCE, 100,000 miles high, was photographed at Sacramento Peak. Loops are known to be associated with sunspots. Their smooth curves may trace visibly the invisible magnetic lines of force that accompany these transient marks on the sun's surface.

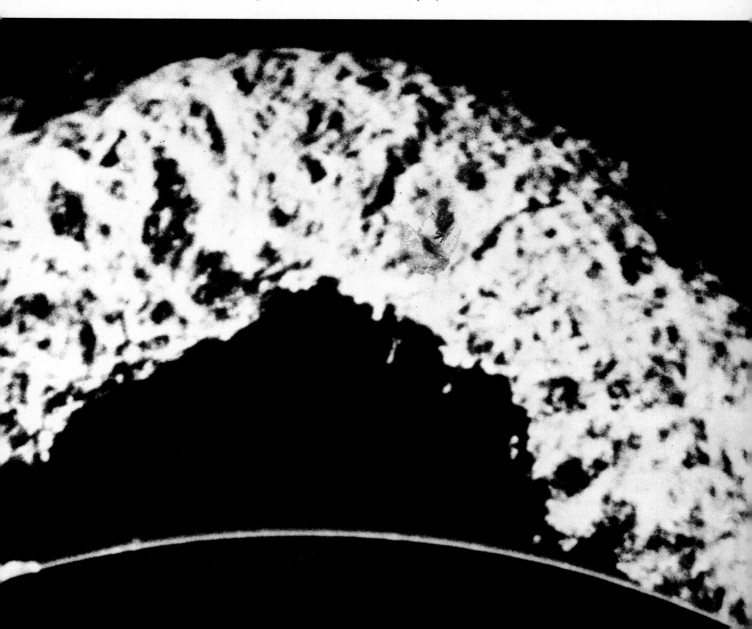

THEORETICAL DEVELOPMENT OF A FAMILY OF PLANETS AND A CENTRAL STAR FROM A CLOUD OF INTERSTELLAR GASES IS SHOWN IN T

How a Solar System Is Formed

One of the most tantalizing mysteries known to man is how the solar system came into being. Of the many solutions proposed, the one that seems to satisfy best the conditions found in and around the solar system was offered by the astronomer Gerard P. Kuiper in the 1950s. This is a refinement of many other theories and is based on the assumption that the sun and all the planets were formed from a cloud of primordial gas *(upper left)*. There are many such clouds in space,

and some of them seem to be in the process of forming stars right now *(page 142)*.

This gas is very thinly distributed in space, but the mutual gravitational attraction of the molecules within the cloud will gradually begin to pull them together into a tighter and tighter mass. This effect is made possible by random whirling movement of gas within the cloud, and is based on the assumption that there will always be some movement in any such cloud.

104

2

4

6

Movement, then, which gradually becomes more rotational, flattens and condenses the cloud (*upper right*). The greatest concentration of matter will be one or more large lumps at the middle, with smaller concentrations streaming around it (*center left*).

In the drawing at center right, the stray lumps of condensing matter are identifiable as a central sun and four protoplanets. The sun is already so condensed that it is beginning to glow with internal nuclear fires, driving away the gases that still surround the protoplanets. As the new star's radiant power grows (*bottom, left*), the gas shells around the near planets are driven off entirely and only naked cores remain. The outer giants are less affected. Finally (*bottom, right*), the bright star's radiation has removed the last of the system's free gases. A mixed array of planets remains—small, solid ones near the star, and much larger, gassy ones farther away.

105

A CHART OF THE MILKY WAY, NORMALLY SEEN AS A BRIGHT RING GIRDLING THE EARTH, IS SHOWN HERE IN A FLAT PROJECTION. IT WAS MADE B

5 What Our Galaxy
Is Made Of

TWO SWEDISH ARTISTS WHO SPENT YEARS DOTTING IN 7,000 INDIVIDUAL STARS ON PHOTOGRAPHS, AND THEN PAINTING IN THE NEBULOUS PARTS

WHEREAS the rough, red face of the sun is broad and pock-marked, every other star in the sky is a fine, faceless shaft of silver light, with neither breadth nor markings. If earth's atmosphere were perfectly transparent and if space around the earth were a perfect void, man's largest telescope, the Palomar 200-inch, would just barely be able to see the largest nearby stars as palpable disks not much more than .0004 inch wide. But this is so minute an image that, in practice, the twinkling fuzziness added to starlight by earth's shimmering layers of air masks it completely. This means that all the stars which spark and spangle space in every direction, whether they look bright as bombs or faint as fireflies, turn out in the telescope to be only dimensionless points of light. Yet these points—pondered as astutely as ends of threads or shreds of tobacco by a Sherlock Holmes—have taught astronomers more about all the other stars together than they know about the nearby sun.

The pinpricks of the stars have presented astronomy with two cardinal questions to answer: *where* are the stars and *what* are they? In the last four decades, after centuries of effort, man has finally learned the answers to both these questions. The stars are tremendous thermonuclear reactors organized by gravity out of gas and arranged in space in inconceivably large systems called galaxies. The sun and the other 7,000-odd stars that can be seen by the unaided eye are simply a few of the inhabitants of one galaxy, the Milky Way.

In the course of finding out how the stars are arranged in space, astronomers with telescopes and angle-measuring devices have accurately sighted over a million stars and recorded their positions in catalogs. But to visualize the universe in perspective they have needed to know the distances to stars as well as the directions. The most straightforward way of finding a star's distance is by measuring its parallax, its apparent annual shift in position against the background of more distant stars. Unhappily, this direct method works well only at fairly short range. Within a distance of 30 light-years, the stars can be positioned with better than 85 per cent accuracy, but only a handful of stars—170 of them —are this close. Beyond 30 light-years, direct parallax measurements become more difficult. Astronomers consider 400 light-years their limit.

BEFORE Friedrich Wilhelm Bessel made the first parallax measurement in 1838, astronomers had the idea that they might be able to estimate a star's distance by its apparent brightness. It seemed possible that all stars might have the same intrinsic brightness if they could only be seen from the same distance away. Working on this assumption, astronomers developed precise methods for measuring the visible brightness or dimness—the magnitude—of stars and hoped that these measurements could be translated some day into distances according to the simple formula: brighter equals closer, fainter equals farther. But when the parallactic distances to nearby stars began to be found, it was clear at once that faintness and brightness do not depend on distance alone, but that some stars actually are much brighter than others. To the naked eye, for instance, the two most luminous stars in the sky are Sirius in Canis Majoris, the Great Dog, and Canopus in Carina, the Southern Hemisphere's constellation of the Keel. It looks as if Sirius is twice as bright as Canopus but it turns out from their parallaxes that Sirius is only 8.7 light-years away, whereas Canopus is 100 light-years away. This means that Canopus really burns not more faintly than Sirius but 65 times as brightly.

Although the brightness yardstick would not work for all stars indiscriminately, astronomers still hoped that it might work for stars of any one kind. To see if it would, they first had to classify the stars near the sun, find their distances by parallax and then seek out faint duplicates of each species on the far horizons. This laborious undertaking, though still in progress, has already proved to be the key to the cosmos, opening the door of human understanding to the enormous distances that separate the stars of the Milky Way from the galaxies beyond. Altogether, many species of stars have been found which do reveal their distances according to the simple formula of brighter-nearer, fainter-farther. One of the most important—because it can be spotted the farthest off—is the

The brightness of a star can be measured in two ways: how bright it seems, and how bright it actually is. This distinction is important to an observer on earth, for a very bright star may be farther away and seem as dim as a feeble nearby star (left). However, in the case of two stars which are at very great distances, it makes little difference if one star is somewhat nearer, since they are both so far away that their relative brightness will remain unchanged when viewed by an observer on the earth.

Cepheid variable, a kind of pulsating star that has the convenient quirk of growing brighter and dimmer in regular periods which depend on its true brilliance. The brighter a Cepheid is on the average, the longer it takes to pulsate. A Cepheid with a 30-day period averages 4,000 times as bright as the sun. One with a one-day period averages only 100 times as bright as the sun. After measuring the pulsation period of a Cepheid, modern astronomers believe they can calculate its average intrinsic brightness—absolute magnitude—with 90 per cent accuracy. By comparing the result with its average visible brightness—apparent magnitude—they can then, with equal accuracy, work out its distance. And they can do this whether the star is a mere 300 light-years away like Polaris, the nearest Cepheid, or over two million light-years away like the Cepheids in the Andromeda nebula, an entirely separate galaxy outside the Milky Way.

Most of the other kinds of stars which serve as distance gauges are not so easily recognizable as Cepheids but they make admirable beacons for judging the remoteness of relatively nearby regions where Cepheids are scarce. In the middle distances of the Milky Way, for instance, astronomers often take advantage of RR Lyrae stars, a pulsating breed that waxes and wanes more rapidly and faintly than do Cepheids. Still other stars of predictable intrinsic brightness can be identified by their spectral lines and the color of their light. One recently devised yardstick—good for a distance of some 2,000 light-years and applicable to common stars like the sun—takes advantage of the strange fact that two of the bright lines emitted by a star's calcium atoms are always wider or narrower depending precisely on the star's over-all brilliance.

Such sophisticated methods might not carry much conviction if it were not for a rough-and-ready way of checking on stellar distances through stellar velocities. Long before astronomers knew that the stars are all circling the center of the galaxy—in fact long before they had any inkling of what a galaxy was—they realized that all the stars they could see were in motion. Under the circumstances nearby stars, like low-flying aircraft, should seem to move rapidly and remote stars, like high-flying aircraft, should seem to creep along.

In using velocities to double check distances, astronomers have perfected careful methods for measuring the various movements of the stars relative to the sun and for subtracting all the apparent movements caused by the earth's own wending, whirling and wobbling in its orbit. Simple star movements across the face of space are called proper motions and measured straightforwardly by small, angular shifts in the celestial coordinates of stars. For some nearby stars it takes only a few years of watching for proper motions to become detectable; for other distant stars it takes centuries.

In addition to proper motions, 19th Century astronomers found that they could measure radial velocities, the motions of stars directly toward or away from the sun. As it travels through space, a star cuts into its own bow wave of light, emitting the successive wave crests closer together than usual. In the same way, the light waves of its wake are slightly pulled apart by its motion away from them. As a result the bow waves become higher in frequency, shorter in wave length and bluer than they would be if the star were lying at celestial anchor. The wake waves become lower in frequency, longer in wave length and redder. The degree of compression or pulling apart is known as the Doppler shift and it is measured by the fact that emission and absorption lines are moved up or down the spectrum by amounts which depend exactly on the speed of the star toward or away from the earth.

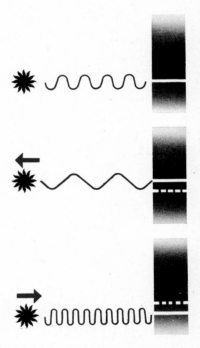

The shifting wave length of a star's light as it moves toward or away from the earth is called the Doppler effect. Light travels in waves (top), and for a star moving rapidly away from the earth (middle) the waves appear to become stretched out— i.e., longer. Since the wave length of red light is longer than that of other visible wave lengths, there is always a shift toward the red end of the spectrum of a receding star. For a star traveling toward the earth (bottom), the waves will appear shortened, and shift toward the blue end of the spectrum. The rate of shift in either direction indicates the speed of the star.

VARIABLE STARS

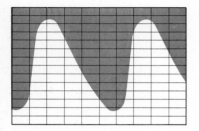

An intrinsic variable is always a single star whose brightness changes depend on changes in its internal nuclear reactions. When nuclear activity is at a peak, the star's light, as shown on the graph above, is brightest. As the activity diminishes, the light dims accordingly and the graph shows a corresponding dip. Some of these stars also change diameters in the process.

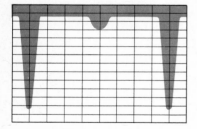

An eclipsing variable consists of a system of two or more stars which circle each other, often a small, bright one and a larger, dimmer partner. When the two bodies are visible, light reaching the earth is brightest; it is dimmest when the smaller star is hidden behind the larger. A small dip in brightness is recorded when the smaller star moves in front of the larger star, and cuts off a little of the latter star's light.

From studying red wakes and blue bow waves, Cepheids and other star types, calcium and other emission or absorption lines, modern astronomers have put two and two together, combined the distances of stars with their motions and come up with a picture of the total, breathtaking, dynamic system in which the sun is just one of 100 billion orbiting participants. Visualizing the whole Milky Way has not been easy. The stars move in circular tracks around the galactic hub, and their real motions are mixtures of apparent motions parallel to the sun and other motions toward or away from it. Stars on the inside lanes can be either catching up with the sun or pulling ahead of it. Stars on the outside lanes can be either dropping back toward the sun or falling away behind it. To compound confusion, many stars travel in clusters, whirling around one another.

Being immersed in the wheel of the Milky Way, man can glimpse only the nearby portions of it, which encircle the earth in a band of stars stretching across and around the skies of both hemispheres. But the concept of the Milky Way as a cosmic island of stars, a single spiral galaxy turning slowly in the immensity of space, became clear once men realized that there were innumerable other galaxies, visible in dozens of perspectives, distributed in all directions outward as far as modern telescopes can see.

The band of the Milky Way is thickest over the Southern Hemisphere because there, beyond the constellation of Sagittarius, is the 10,000- to 15,000-light-year-thick hub of the galaxy, a bright, bulbous, pumpkin-shaped region packed with huge red stars, shrouded in clouds of dust and "visible" mainly in infrared and radio waves. Outside the hub and revolving around it is a disk of stars and star stuff spanning a diameter of 100,000 light-years, an inconceivable 600 million billion miles. Within the disk, arms of dark dust and gas, sleeved in the bejeweling brilliance of countless giant stars, spiral outward from the hub like showers of sparks around a prodigious pin wheel. Whereas many bright stars in the hub are red, the bright stars in the arms are blue. The sun is neither. Being only a fifth-magnitude star, up to 100,000 times fainter than its brightest neighbors, it does not add to the blue brilliance of the spiral arms but shines with a mild yellow light. It is located 30,000 light-years, or three quarters of the way, out from the hub, and orbits around it once every 200 million years.

THE sun and all the other myriad stars which stay in the gassy, dusty main disk of the Milky Way are only one of the galaxy's two principal populations. Their pancake-shaped array, for all its vastness, is roughly equivalent to the disk of planets around the sun. But the Milky Way also has a much larger part: a dustless, spherical halo of stars and star clusters, 100,000 light-years in diameter—equivalent to the distant sphere of comets that surrounds both the sun and the planets. Like the hub stars, many of the bright stars of the halo are red and are thought to be elder stellar citizens, dating back to the galaxy's birth.

The star clusters of the halo are almost miniature galaxies in their own right, each containing tens of thousands of tightly packed, bright stars. Since they are globular in shape they have been named—without much inspiration—globular clusters. Outside of the clusters the halo also has several billion individual stars traveling alone on rakishly tilted orbits that take them vaulting up out of the disk in all directions. A few of them have been found actually in the disk in the regions near the sun. One telltale trait by which they are recognized is their apparent high velocity. Not that they are really hurrying around the hub any faster than other stars, but they seem to be because they do not travel on arcs parallel to the sun's but swoop by the disk from above or below, passing right through it and out the other side at speeds of from 50 to 200 miles per second.

While charting the Milky Way and discovering where the stars are, astronomers have also learned what they are. The same observations about brightness which led to distance calculations also led to knowledge of star sizes and masses. The long studies with spectroscopes, filters, photoelectric cells and thermocouples which made it possible to find star species that would serve as beacons and yardsticks also led to an astonishing amount of detailed knowledge about stars—knowledge that revealed the seemingly monotonous multitudes of the heavens as a most motley crew, distinguished by an infinite variety of unexpected conditions and situations.

To appreciate the infinite variety that the stars show, one must have some idea how astronomers can acquire information at long-distance, as they do. One might think, for example, that gassy structures like stars cannot differ much in their magnetic properties or, if they do, that astronomers could never find out about it anyway. But they do and astronomers can. The spectral lines of light emitted in magnetic fields are split into double or triple lines, separated by gaps which are broad or narrow, depending on the magnetic-field strength. From measuring the gaps—the Zeeman splitting—Mount Wilson's Horace W. Babcock has measured this strength for hundreds of stars and found that they vary from one or two gauss, like the sun, up to 34,000 gauss for a fast-spinning star, like HD 215441. The undoubtedly weird effects which such huge magnetic fields have on the flares and sunspots of such stars have yet to be calculated, but if any of these stars has inhabited planets, the beings on them must be able to generate all the electricity they need simply by laying out coils of copper on the ground and letting planetary rotation do the rest.

Another extraordinary feat of the spectrograph is measuring how fast stars rotate. Even though the advancing and retreating edges of a star are merged in its infinitesimal light shaft, the Doppler shift can still be gauged. Because of rotation the atoms of each element on the star's surface are either advancing and showing blue, retreating and showing red, or keeping their distance. The net result of the combined reddening and bluing is smudged spectral lines, widened in a manner that tells exactly how fast the star is spinning.

At the equator, most small stars like the sun are moving at only one or two miles per second, but many of the massive stars are found to be spinning dizzily at speeds of up to 200 miles per second. The reason probably is that some big stars, in their formative years, condense so quickly and start spinning so brilliantly and abruptly that they are not slowed much by the elastic magnetic spokes they create around themselves in the gas clouds out of which they form. What happens to a fast-spinning star after its birth is exemplified by Pleione, one of the brightest of the Pleiades cluster. Pleione's equator rotates at 190 miles per second, with the result that it constantly hurls hydrogen off into space, girdling its waist in a ring of gas that glows with excitement from Pleione's intense ultraviolet rays. The fact that most small stars spin far more slowly than Pleione is thought to indicate that small stars are generally girdled by rings of planets, which helped, at their formation, to slow them down.

THE two work horses of stellar astronomy are temperature and brightness measurements. This is not because temperature and brightness are the two most valuable pieces of information about stars but because they are the only two pieces of information which can be had readily. Taking a star's temperature can be done in several ways: it is simply a matter of finding out in what section of the spectrum the star shines most brightly. In general, if it is brightest in red light, it is a cool star; if it is brightest in yellow light, it is a warm star; and if it is brightest in blue light, it is a hot star. In similar fashion, the over-all brightness of a star can be ascertained through measuring the intensities of its light at many wave lengths and adding them all up.

Of all stellar characteristics, one of the most important to know is mass. From the mass of a star—the amount of matter in it—modern astrophysicists can calculate roughly what all its other properties should be after it has been alight for any given number of years. By the same token, they can calculate how old a star is from the way it is shining—as long as they first know how much matter there is in it. Unfortunately the mass of a star is often the most elusive and indirect of its vital statistics.

The only kind of star in which mass can be measured in a straightforward way is a double star: a system of two stars revolving around one another in orbits shaped by their mutual gravitation. From the length of time they take to revolve and the distance they keep between them, their masses can be figured out easily by Newton's laws of gravitation. By happy circumstance, 75 per cent of the stars do have one or more companions with which they dance as they go down the galactic track. Often they circle their orbiting mates so closely that they seem to be single stars when they are really pairs, triumvirates or gangs. Antares in Scorpio, the 16th most brilliant star in the sky, is actually two stars. Capella and Alpha Centauri are each three; Castor is six.

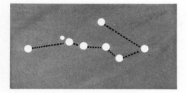

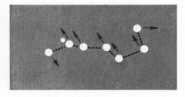

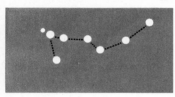

The shape of the Big Dipper changes over the years as a result of unequal rates of movement among its stars. No constellation, immutable as it may seem, can escape being eventually distorted out of recognition by the movements of the stars that make it up. The Big Dipper consists of seven stars, the five middle ones apparently closely bunched and moving in about the same direction and at about the same speed. However, the single stars at each end are nearer the earth and appear to travel much faster. In another hundred thousand years the familiar dipper shape, as viewed from the earth, will be gone.

THE first two stars recognized as parts of a single gravitational unit were the two brightest members of Castor, studied by William Herschel in 1803. The first double—or binary—star to be merely noticed, however, was Mizar at the bend of the Big Dipper's handle, which showed up in the newfangled telescopes of 1650 to be two stars where only one had been seen before. In 1889 the bright companion of the same Mizar partnership was further subdivided in another victory for the miraculous, all-purpose spectroscope, which dissected its light into two separate rainbows alternately overlapping one another. Since 1889 the number of multicomponent stars made visible by the telescope has been increased by an even larger number revealed through the spectroscope. Some of them, like UV Puppis, orbit so closely that they roll around one another's multi-million-mile equators in under two hours flat. Others, like Beta Lyrae, swap star stuff through the crests of huge tidal waves and are wrapped in turbulence.

Of all the strange multiple stars disclosed by the telescope and spectroscope, only the simple double stars reveal their masses. This is because the tempos and patterns of three-star tangos, four-star fandangos and many-star mazurkas are often too complicated even for modern mathematics. Luckily, however, many multiple stars are binaries, and it is from these examples that astronomers know how much matter there is in stars in general. From each item of such knowledge flows a great deal of other knowledge. Star UW Canis Majoris in the Great Dog, for instance, is a double star with a total mass 36 times that of the sun's. From this and the fact that this UW pair is 10,000 times as bright as the sun, astrophysicists can calculate that the pair will burn out and die in a mere 300,000-year moment of eternity. Moreover they can be reasonably sure that a single star like Rigel in Orion, which is similar to UW Canis Majoris in other respects, must have a similar mass and a similar future.

Through virtuoso use of instruments—uncovering tremendous truths in tiny fractions and nuances—astronomers have sorted out the many-complexioned stars of the Milky Way by their masses, brightnesses, temperatures, compositions, spins and magnetic strengths and have found that they fall into two principal groups: normal stars and abnormal stars. The normal stars are normal for two reasons: they are in the majority, especially in the regions of the Milky Way near the sun, and they burn in the manner in which astrophysicists expect stars to burn. Given fusion, astrophysicists can calculate how stars made of hydrogen ought to shine. Massive stars, in which the force of gravity jams the fuel most quickly and forcefully toward the center, ought to burn far more rapidly than lightweight stars, in which the central hydrogen fuel is packed less densely. Because of their gravitational stoking and corresponding temperature, big stars generate more energy than small stars do. In terms of what can be seen, they must burn brightly blue and hot, while medium-sized stars must burn moderately warm and yellow and small stars must burn dimly cool and red.

This exact hierarchy of brightness and color, as calculated by astrophysicists, was actually observed by astronomers long before anyone knew a fission from a fusion. It was discovered by plotting the brilliances of stars on a graph against their spectral types. The spectral types were arbitrarily divided into O, B, A, F, G, K and M, a classification which is still remembered by college students with help from the Harvard-coined sentence, "Oh, Be A Fine Girl: Kiss Me." As the nature of light became better understood, it was realized that each spectral type represents a range of color and temperature. Massive, brilliant O-stars at one end of the spectrum are hot and blue and range from 90,000° down to 45,000° F. in surface temperature. They are so hot that most of their energy is emitted in invisible ultraviolet rays. Lightweight, dim M-stars, at the other end of the spectrum, are cool and red and range from 6,000° down to 3,000° F. They are so cool that most of their energy is invisible infrared heat rays. Mild, yellow middleweight G-stars like the sun fall at the center of the spectrum. They range in temperature from 10,000° down to 9,000° F., and emit almost all their energy in the visible fraction of the spectrum.

WHEN the various kinds of normal stars are set out on a graph—brightness plotted against spectral type—they fall on a line sloping downward from hot blue O-stars in the upper left to cool red M-stars in the lower right. G-stars like the sun occupy a "satisfying," average sort of position near the center of the graph. The line on which normal stars plot out on the graph has come to be known as the "main sequence." This splendid agreement between astrophysical theory and astronomical observation as to what should be and what actually is scarcely filled either party with jubilation because, from the start, there were all sorts of abnormal stars which did not fall on the main-sequence line in the color-brightness graph and did not satisfy the thermonuclear requirements of early atomic theory. Most of these abnormal stars were overbright for their spectral type and thus plotted out above the main-sequence line on the color-brightness graph. At one end of the spectrum there were overbright "blue supergiants" like Rigel in Orion which is 800 light-years away but maintains status as the seventh brightest star in the sky by pouring out energy at the astonishing rate of 40,000 suns. At the other end of the spectrum from blue supergiants the roster of abnormal stars included red giants like Arcturus, in Boötes, No. 4 star in the heavens, and red supergiants like Betelgeuse, in Orion, the ninth brightest star. In between these two extremes there were overbright white, yellow and orange giants and supergiants—and also a puzzling assortment of pulsating and exploding stars: brilliant orange and yellow

Cepheids, less brilliant white RR Lyrae stars and bluish exploding stars of fantastic billion-sun brightness that are known as supernovae.

Just how peculiar some of the abnormal overbright stars are is illustrated by Betelgeuse, the red supergiant in Orion. In spectral type, Betelgeuse is only a red M-star, shedding its ruddy light from a surface half as hot as the sun's. Normal M-stars are 10 times smaller in diameter and 1,000 times dimmer in light than the sun. But Betelgeuse equals 500 suns in diameter and 17,000 suns in brightness. At the outer edges of its dark substance, huge currents of billowing gas are rising and falling more quickly than the whole globe of the star is rotating. And in these convection currents the atoms are more loosely packed than in the most perfect vacuum man can create on earth.

As well as overbright abnormal stars, there are also underbright ones that plot out below the main-sequence line on the color-brightness graph. Erupting stars called novae are normally dim for their color but grow periodically overbright during flare-ups and hurl off celestial smoke rings of gas and dust into the space around them. Still farther downward in the color-brightness graph fall the extremely underbright stars called "white dwarfs." Though dim and small, these dwarfs each contain about as much matter as the sun but cram it densely into volumes as small as the planet Mercury's and weighing anywhere from one to 20 or more tons per cubic inch. Presumably the reason that the matter in white dwarfs does not explode with new nuclear transformations under such fantastically tight packing is that all of it has already been converted into nuclear ash—atoms incapable of any more reactions.

THE fact that white dwarfs seem to be dying stars and that most of the other abnormal stars are actively unstable—or at least bloated in a way that augurs ill for their future stability—convinces astronomers that abnormal stars are suffering the maladies of old age. Yet it is important to realize that abnormal dying stars are a tiny minority of all stars. Most varieties of abnormal stars—revealed by examples found in double-star combinations—are from one to 30 times as massive as the sun. Because they are big they are short-lived. Stars of the sun's mass and smaller are long-lived and have not yet had time to become abnormal. And they are overwhelmingly numerous in comparison to the sick heavy stars.

For every ultraviolet Rigel, 30 times as massive, 40,000 times as bright and probably 100,000 times as short-lived as the sun, there exist 200,000 yellow suns and several million faint red M-stars smaller than the sun. The true nature of the Milky Way's average citizens can be glimpsed best in the sun's own cosmic backyard. Within 16 light-years of the sun there are 50 stars: 28 singles, eight doubles and two triples. In addition there are five unseen companions, either minuscule stars or enormous planets which cannot be seen but only detected by the kinks they put in the motions of the stars with which they are associated. Of the 50 bona fide stars in the sun's neighborhood, four are white dwarfs, already burned out, two are fast-living, ultrabright A-stars, one is a brilliant yellow-white F-star, two are mild yellow G-stars like the sun, seven are small orange K-stars, and 34 are tiny common-as-star-dust M-stars.

Evidently, in its own "local swimming hole," as Palomar's Walter Baade used to call it, the sun really is quite a big frog. But the majority of ruddy-skinned tadpole stars around the sun have one great superiority. According to modern views of stellar evolution, the tadpoles will remain alight 10 to 200 times longer than the sun—billions of years after the sun has gone out.

HORSEHEAD NEBULA, A CLOUD OF COOL DUST, REARS ITSELF AGAINST A BACKDROP OF HOT GAS GLOWING WITH ENERGY FROM NEARBY STARS

Gas, Dust and Stars

The stupendous system of the Milky Way embodies not only the visible stars in all their kinds, but also streaming clouds of gas and dust like the Horsehead nebula above. These cosmic mists are more rarefied than the highest laboratory vacuum, but in many regions of the Milky Way they are banked so deep, cloud on cloud, that they completely hide the stars and galaxies which lie behind them.

THE MILKY WAY'S TRUE NATURE is revealed in this remarkable photograph taken in the Southern Hemisphere with red-sensitive emulsion. Since red light penetrates gas, the normally obscured hub of the Milky Way and the central parts of the disk around it show up as those of a typical galaxy in deep space. The three dark bars are braces supporting the film holder.

Structure of the Galaxy

The greatest single advance in man's modern understanding of the stars is his discovery that they are arranged in galaxies and that all stars visible to the naked eye belong to one galaxy, our own Milky Way. Appreciating the Milky Way's galactic shape is difficult because the sun and earth are immersed in it. But pictures like the ones above and opposite, which give the "look" of the Milky Way in wave lengths of radiation not normally visible, show that the sun is part of a vast, wheeling disk of stars, dust and gas, 100,000 light-years wide, revolving around a central hub. The gas streaming out from the hub is lit by brilliant blue stars. The hub itself is mostly red, and so is a diffuse halo of stars around it which are not confined to the main galactic disk.

THE MILKY WAY'S NEAR TWIN is this galaxy, NGC 891, seen through the 200-inch telescope 20 million light-years away. Although smaller than the Milky Way, NGC 891 has a disk of dust encircling its hub and a degree of flattening which resemble Milky Way features as they would look from the outside.

THE MILKY WAY'S EXTERIOR would have a spiral shape if seen from above *(top drawing)*, and a lens shape if seen from the side *(bottom)*. These reconstructions are based on analysis of radio waves broadcast by interstellar gas in spiral arms. The crosses mark the center of the galaxy and the position of the sun, 30,000 light-years from the center. Before the invention of radio astronomy, only those fragments of spiral arms marked by the yellow lines in the top drawing had been seen and mapped. But since then, radio astronomers have tuned in more of the Milky Way's gas clouds and have mapped all the areas indicated in red.

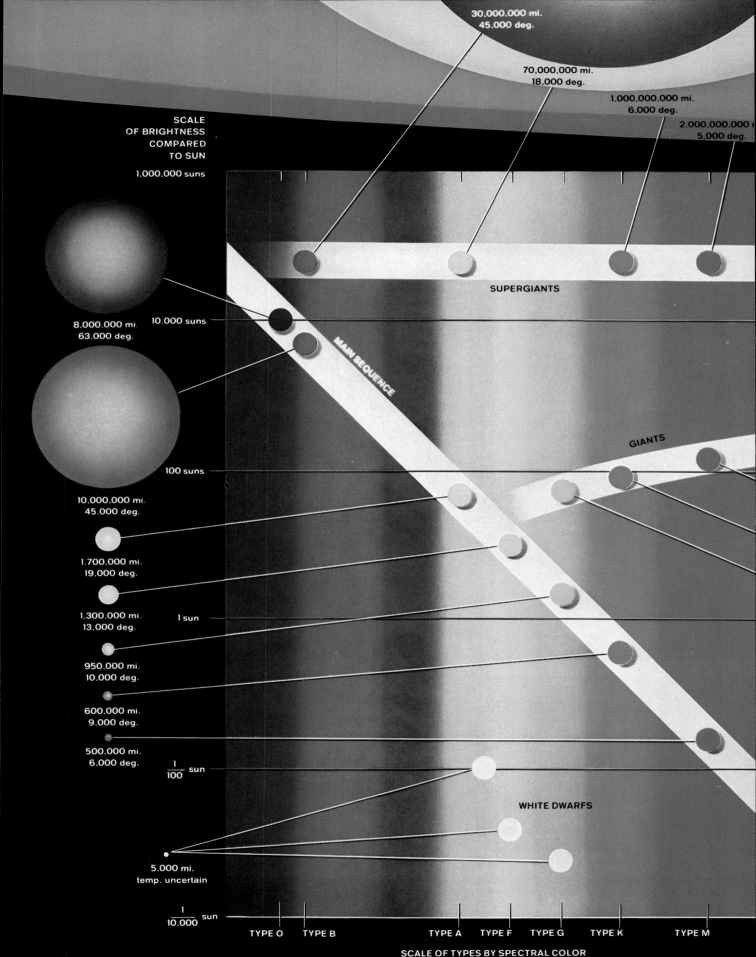

30,000,000 mi.
45,000 deg.

70,000,000 mi.
18,000 deg.

1,000,000,000 mi.
6,000 deg.

2,000,000,000 mi
5,000 deg.

SCALE
OF BRIGHTNESS
COMPARED
TO SUN

1,000,000 suns

8,000,000 mi.
63,000 deg.

10,000 suns

SUPERGIANTS

MAIN SEQUENCE

100 suns

GIANTS

10,000,000 mi.
45,000 deg.

1,700,000 mi.
19,000 deg.

1,300,000 mi.
13,000 deg.

1 sun

950,000 mi.
10,000 deg.

600,000 mi.
9,000 deg.

500,000 mi.
6,000 deg.

$\frac{1}{100}$ sun

WHITE DWARFS

5,000 mi.
temp. uncertain

$\frac{1}{10,000}$ sun

TYPE O   TYPE B   TYPE A   TYPE F   TYPE G   TYPE K   TYPE M

SCALE OF TYPES BY SPECTRAL COLOR

NOTE: THE FIGURES PRINTED UNDER OR IN EACH STAR
REPRESENT ITS DIAMETER IN MILES
AND ITS SURFACE TEMPERATURE IN DEGREES FAHRENHEIT

60,000,000 mi.
5,500 deg.

17,000,000 mi.
7,000 deg.

7,000,000 mi.
9,000 deg.

How the Astronomers
Sort Stars into Families

For a man trying to puzzle some order out of the different kinds of stars that hang in the sky, there are two important clues, both provided by the stars themselves. These are a star's color, and its true brightness. If color and brightness are plotted on a graph such as the one at left, some very revealing family relationships among stars are disclosed.

Reading the diagram is simple: bright stars are located near the top of the rainbow-hued rectangle, and dim ones at the bottom. Hot blue stars are at the left, medium-hot white and yellow ones in the middle, and cool red ones at the right.

• One other clue that astronomers have to help them is that color and brightness are related, and that both depend on the size of the star. Normally a small star will be red and dim because it is not big enough to burn any hotter. If it is a little larger it will be able to sustain more intense nuclear fires and it will burn yellow. Larger still, it will be very hot, very bright, and will be blue. Thus, when an assortment of stars is plotted on the graph, most of them will fall somewhere on a line slanting down from left to right, with the large hot blue stars at top left, and the small dim cool red ones at the lower right. This slanting line consists of so-called "normal" stars whose color-brightness-size relationship is proper for healthy stars. It includes most stars in the sky and is known to astronomers as the "main sequence."

• In addition to normal main-sequence stars, there are several kinds of abnormal stars. One family, called "red giants," is considered abnormal because its members give off much more light than a small red star should—which simply means that they are much bigger than an ordinary healthy red star ought to be. Their position on the graph is in the red section to the right and fairly high up, since they are about 100 times as bright as the sun.

• Similarly there is a varicolored family of even brighter stars, which means that they must be even bigger than red giants. They are called "supergiants," and their position is across the top of the graph since all of them are more than 10,000 times as bright as the sun.

• Last is a family of little dim stars known as "white dwarfs," so tiny that they should be red, but most of them are actually white or yellow. These are shrunken—often to planet size—because nuclear processes have ceased in their cores and there is no energy left to resist the crush of gravity. In fact they are dying stars. Their density is extreme, their surfaces abnormally hot because their minute size provides insufficient radiating surface.

• Relative sizes of some representative stars are shown around the edges of the diagram. When drawn to the same scale, the supergiants are so large that only their lower edges can be seen curving across the top of the picture. Only the dot for the white dwarfs is exaggerated. If it were in scale it would be so small as to be invisible.

Plotting the Ages of Stars

Once astronomers had sorted out the common types of stars as shown on pages 118-119, they had a standard for appraising the oddities. They could then plot graphs for specific groups of stars and study their peculiarities. The two color-brightness graphs on these pages show how this led to one of astronomy's most important discoveries—the distinction between young and old star populations.

As individual graphs were plotted for more and more star groups, it became apparent that one of two distinct patterns always showed up. One of these patterns is indicated by the white areas in the graph to the left, and the other by the white areas in the graph to the right. But while the patterns themselves were clear enough on the graphs, the realization of what they meant came only gradually.

Over several decades clues piled up that indi-

YOUNG STARS form this pattern on the color-brightness graph. Locations are shown for the main types of young stars and for a typical star group, the Pleiades.

AN EXAMPLE OF THE YOUNG STARS PLOTTED ABOVE IS THE EXTREMELY YOUTHFUL PLEIADES CLUSTER, DISPLAYING ITS TYPICAL HOT BLUE COL

cated the patterns were related to the ages of star groups, one pattern *(left)* for young stars, the other *(right)* for old stars. Groups which were known to be young, like the Pleiades *(below left),* always showed up in the left-hand pattern. Groups of old stars, like the globular cluster Messier 3, always showed up in the right-hand pattern. Thus, as the basic color-brightness graph had become a standard for comparing stars with each other, special forms of the graph became a gauge for comparing ages.

With this age-pattern established for a sampling of the stars, it was now possible to extend the same concept to all of them. Gradually it was learned that stars are not scattered haphazardly but that their locations are related to their age: the very young and the very old consort with their own kind and so make up two distinct populations in the skies.

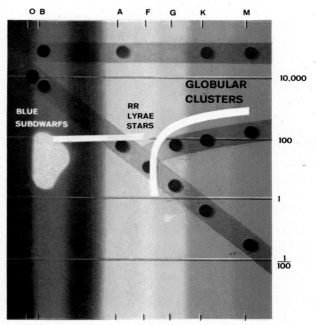

OLD STARS form this pattern on the above color-brightness graph. The oldest stars of all, like those of Messier 3 *(below),* are located in globular clusters.

N EXAMPLE OF THE OLD STARS PLOTTED IN THE GRAPH ABOVE IS THE GLOBULAR CLUSTER MESSIER 3, SHOWING ITS TYPICAL WEAK YELLOW COLOR

Bizarre Unstable Stars

The great majority of abnormal stars are bloated giants and supergiants which, although they may be using energy at a feverish pace, do it in a fairly steady way. Rarer kinds of abnormal stars are far less stable and often spew out dust and gas unpredictably, or even vanish in mammoth explosions. Planetaries like the Dumb-Bell nebula at right or the Ring nebula on page 50 are stars which have emitted huge opalescent globes of gas—as if they were blowing cosmic soap bubbles around themselves. The rare breed of UV Ceti stars sometimes spout flares which outshine the stars themselves. Novae periodically erupt. Supernovae explode outright in clouds of debris like the Crab nebula on pages 140-141. Cepheids and RR Lyrae stars burn hot and cold, bright and dim, like candles in a wind.

All these forms of stellar instability are thought to afflict stars which have already gone through gianthood or supergianthood. Probably the upheavals arise from internal readjustments between thermonuclear fuel and fire—adjustments akin to the flare-up of a half-burned log settling on the hearth.

Planetaries like the one at right are so named because their pale green or blue bubbles, seen with small telescopes, look like the orbs of distant planets. Their central stars are smaller than the sun but denser, hotter and bluer. Their outer globes of gas, one to 10 trillion miles across, are propelled outward relatively slowly at 20,000 to 100,000 mph. What impels them is unknown, but it may be sheer radiation force.

DUMB-BELL NEBULA in Vulpecula is a sphere of gas hurled off by a small hot blue star at its center. The star's ultraviolet rays make the gas fluoresce colorfully. The central regions, which contain the most gas, glow hotter and bluer than the thin red outer edges.

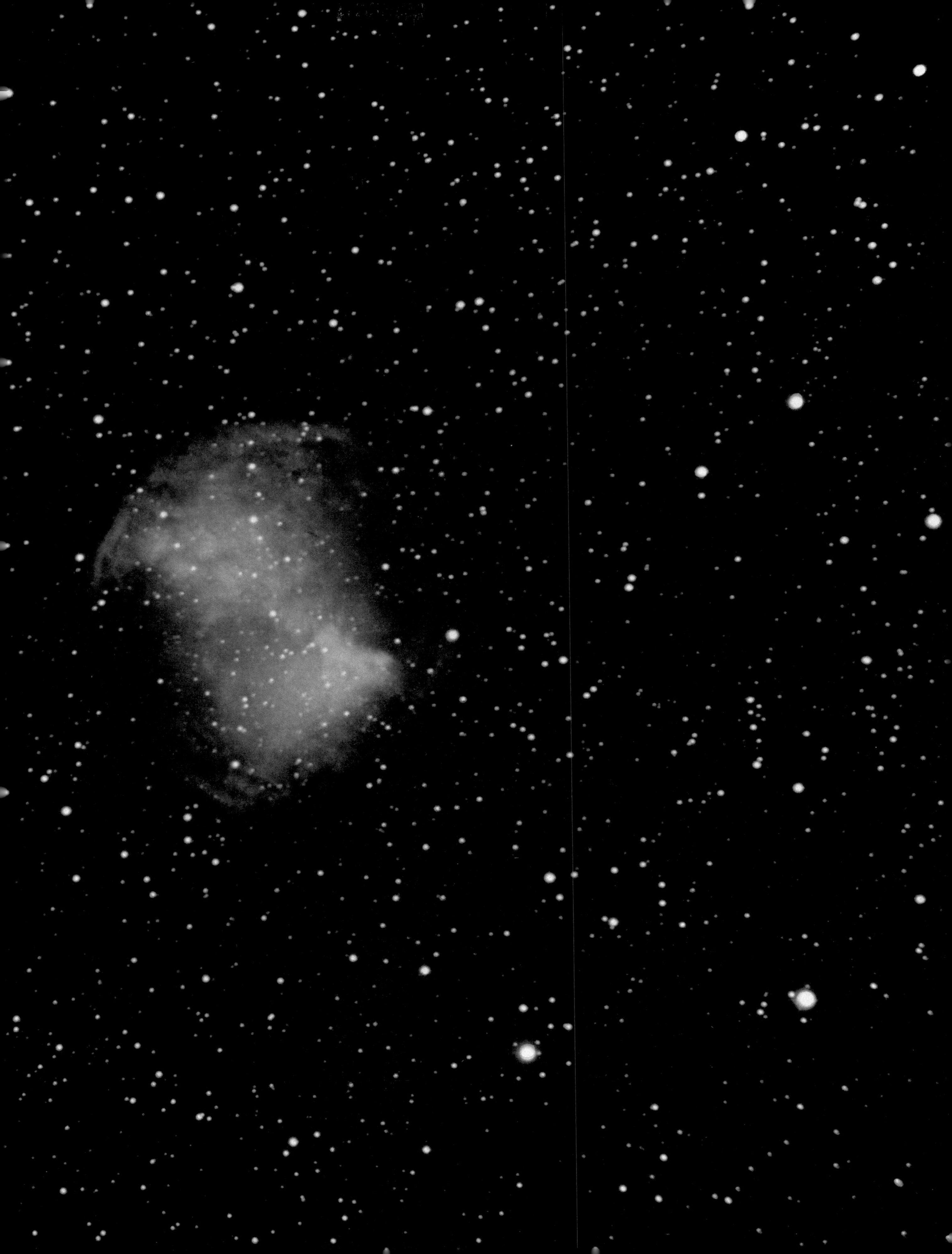

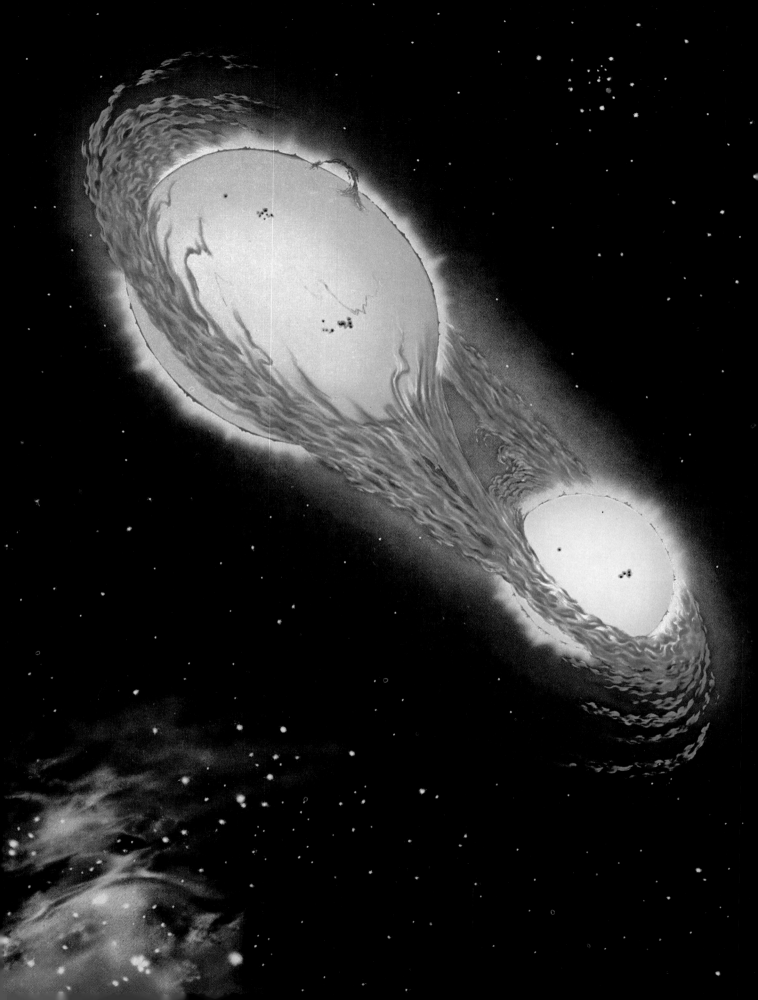

ZETA CANCRI'S STELLAR TRIPLETS CONSIST OF AN ORANGE GIANT, A NORMAL WHITE STAR AND A YELLOW STAR THAT ORBITS THE OTHER TWO

Stars That Travel in Tandem

The variety of stars—blue, yellow or red, normal or giant, pulsating, exploding or extinguished—is further enriched by coupling, tripling or clustering. Only one out of four stars travels alone. Of the others, roughly a third are double stars and the rest are multiples. Almost all these knots of stars seem single to the eye. Most seem single even through the telescope. The closest partners can be detected only by the spectroscope, which can separate the twin rainbows in their light.

When double stars revolve closely, like the com-

ponents of U Cephei (*opposite*), they exchange gas in tidal prominences which flow across between their gravitationally distorted equators. A more complex three-star system is Zeta Cancri (*above*), in which the two left-hand stars revolve every 60 years and the third is their satellite, orbiting them every 1,150 years. Partnerships may be made of nearly all types. Often they seem mismatched—tiny red stars with supergiants, or sunlike stars with white dwarfs. But no matter how oddly mated, the components of each system are thought to have been born together.

GG-SHAPED because of mutual gravitational attraction, and
reaming gas emitted by the larger partner, the twin stars of
Cephei—a big orange and a smaller blue—circle each other.

THE VEIL NEBULA, a diaphanous filigree of star-spangled red, white and blue in Cygnus the Swan, is part of what once must have been the outer layers of an unstable star. Today, still impelled by a stellar eruption or explosion some 50,000 years ago, the star's fragments have become a globe of gas some 300 trillion miles wide, still hurtling outward at 300,000 mph. The

outrushing gas is moving fastest at its leading edge and more slowly inside. Colliding with mists in space, the fast particles in it emit blue light, the slow particles trailing along behind emit white or red light. As in all other color photographs of stars and nebulae on these pages, the colors are real ones which the naked eye would be able to see if it were sensitive enough.

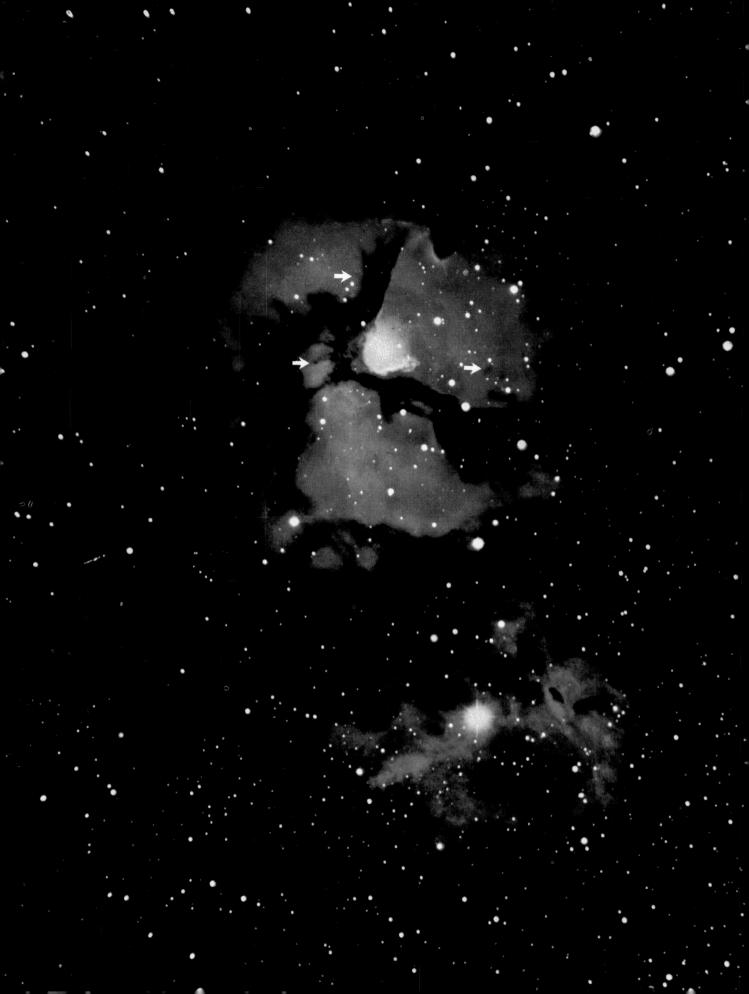

6

The Birth and Death of Stars

HAVING cataloged the many-complexioned stars and discovered where and what they are, astronomers and astrophysicists have turned increasingly to the question of how: how did the stars come to be where and what they are? Out of such inquiries the outline of a great intelligible scheme has emerged, a scheme which not only orders the dumfounding diversity of the stars into evolutionary sequences but also explains all the troublesome, abnormal species of stars as simply stages in the lives of normal stars. Many details of the grand picture remain to be inked in: the individual quirks and foibles of stars need to be measured with more precision, and the titanic forces that shape stellar destinies need to be corralled more securely in equations. But already calculations and observations agree well enough to give a description of the birth, adolescence, maturity, senility and death of most stars and even, in a roughly quantitative way, of the ultimate ends of time when the stars of the Milky Way must all fade and wink out.

The credit for this great accomplishment—easily the greatest in the last 15 years of astronomy—belongs to hundreds of scientists. On the theoretical side one pioneering thinker was the English astronomer Sir Arthur Stanley

Eddington. It was Eddington, in the 1920s, who first realized the importance of mass in a star's life. He saw that once a star has been formed with a certain amount of matter in it, the rest of its life is determined by a constant tug of war between two opposite tendencies. On the one hand a star tends to contract under its own gravitational bulk and on the other it tends to fly apart through release of the energy contained in it by virtue of Einstein's $E=mc^2$ law. In Eddington's time the exact thermonuclear mechanisms for releasing this energy were still mysterious. Once they became known in the late 1930s, other theorists —notably Subrahmanyan Chandrasekhar, Hans Bethe and Carl von Weizsäcker—were able to extend Eddington's ideas and calculate what sort of life a star of given mass should have.

ON the observational side the fundamental idea for coming to grips with stellar evolution was worked out in the 1940s by Palomar's Walter Baade. Baade pointed out that, just as there are different floras and faunas on the separated islands and continents of earth, so there are also different populations of stars in the sky which have evolved in isolation from one another. In Baade's view, a population of stars known to have come into being all at one time should reveal an evolutionary pattern by the kinds of stars left shining in it. In applying this concept, Baade distinguished between just two populations: the halo stars which form the spheres that surround galaxies, and the disk stars which orbit in the main, wheel-shaped thoroughfares of spiral galaxies like the Milky Way.

Baade discovered that halo stars are mostly reddish, dominated by the light of distended, overbright red giants like Arcturus. He also discovered that they inhabit regions devoid of dust and gas out of which new stars could form. Putting two and two together, he deduced that halo stars are an old population from which the normal complement of massive, fast-burning blue stars has already perished. The survivors are mainly small, normal yellow and red stars. The few abnormal red giants among them are the most massive stars left in the population and they are abnormal because it has come their turn to sicken and die. When they have joined their more massive brethren in the moribund state of white dwarfdom, the next group of less massive halo stars will be aging in their turn (*they* will be the red giants of their day) and so it will go for billions of years until the last, least massive, longest-lived halo star of all enters upon its final death throes and finally goes out, leaving the halo dark.

In contrast to halo stars, disk stars are surrounded by plenty of raw material for the making of new stars. Most of this star stuff is contained in the swirling gas and dust clouds of the disk's spiral arms. Baade observed that stars along the spiral arms are generally much more blue and brilliant—much more massive and fast-burning—than stars elsewhere in a galaxy. He concluded that they must be new stars and that disk stars in general must be a mixed, relatively young population, replenished constantly by fresh stars of all sizes, born out of the primordial gas and dust clouds. In consequence disk stars should be of all types and ages: new blue massive stars, new to moderately aged middleweight stars, and new to old lightweight stars.

Baade's concept of separate stellar populations proved to be one of the most brilliant and fruitful insights of 20th Century science. Other observers—notably Palomar's Allan Sandage—refined Baade's idea and applied it to the disk and halo stars of the Milky Way. Instead of working with the whole halo population at once, they studied its globular clusters separately. They reasoned that the whole halo might not have come into being at exactly the same time but that the thousands of stars in any single cluster were almost certainly all about the same age. Accordingly, they measured the brightness and colors of many thousands of stars in several of the Milky Way's globular clusters and plotted them, cluster by cluster, on color-brightness graphs. They found that the least massive stars in each cluster fell on the main-sequence line of normal star-types, that a narrow range of middleweight stars had swung away from the main-sequence line and become overbright and abnormal, and finally that all the most massive stars had vanished altogether—presumably having subsided into invisibility as white dwarfs. The cutoff point, above which there were no more normal stars, turned out to be different in each cluster and gave a final clue to the age of the cluster. Some youngish clusters still had stars a fraction more massive than the sun. Some clusters were so old that quite possibly they no longer had *any* normal stars that were as massive as the sun.

The same technique of analysis has also been applied to stars in clusters in the disk of the Milky Way. It reveals that disk clusters—or galactic clusters as they are confusingly called—are just as mixed in age as Baade suspected they would be. Some disk clusters—traveling in the dust-free and gas-free lanes in the spiral arms—consist of such uniformly small stars that they must be at least three times as old as the sun. Still others in the cloud-rich spiral arms contain such massive short-lived stars that the clusters are thought to be only hundreds of thousands of years old. In the newest of all clusters the least massive stars have not even had time yet to finish being born. They are already dimly alight but their positions on a color-brightness graph show that they are still contracting from their primordial clouds. So great, however, is the difference made by mass in a star's rate of living and dying that a single, newborn cluster may have its least massive stars still contracting in the pangs of birth and its most massive stars already beginning to grow overbright, abnormal and senile.

The statistical evidence of stellar evolution, gained in an observational way by comparing and relating the traits of stars on graphs, has been bulwarked conclusively by theoretical calculations. Following in the footsteps of Eddington and later theorists but taking advantage of modern nuclear knowledge and high-speed electronic computers, Princeton's Martin Schwarzschild, Cambridge's Fred Hoyle and a number of other theorists have carefully worked out the probable lives of stars of various masses and have reached answers so close to the observed facts that it seems impossible for either the mathematicians or the observers to be far wrong.

THE story of a star begins with its birth, an event little different from the birth of the sun already described. A cloud of dust and gas, whirled into pockets of high density, begins to contract around one or more of its gravitational centers. Many centers in one tight cloud can result in a single star plus planets, a multiple star, or a multiple star plus planets. The finished product depends on the density and size of the original cloud and on the degree of rough-and-tumble in its movements. Astronomers believe that they may see unlit protostars in the very act of contracting in the nearby clouds of the Milky Way's spiral arms. They appear as dark globules against the less opaque regions of gas and dust around them.

When a protostar contracts, its central regions are warmed by the release of gravitational energy—the heat of infalling atoms colliding with one another. Eventually the heat becomes so intense that the hydrogen of the core begins to fuse into helium. At first the nuclear fusions of single atoms are infrequent and

THE COLOR OF STARS

Although they all look whitish to the naked eye, the 25 brightest stars are of several different colors. Each color, which is an indication of the spectral type of the star, has been given its own letter designation (i.e., G for yellow stars, M for red stars) by astronomers. The complete order of spectral colors is shown at the bottom of the diagram on pages 118-119.

STAR	SPECTRAL TYPE	COLOR
Sirius	A	white
Canopus	F	yellow-white
a Centauri	G	yellow
Arcturus	K	orange
Vega	A	white
Capella	G	yellow
Rigel	B	blue-white
Procyon	F	yellow-white
Betelgeuse	M	red
Achernar	B	blue-white
b Centauri	B	blue-white
Altair	A	white
a Crucis	B	blue-white
Aldebaran	K	orange
Spica	B	blue-white
Antares	M	red
Pollux	K	orange
Fomalhaut	A	white
Deneb	A	white
b Crucis	B	blue-white
Regulus	B	blue-white
Adhara	B	blue-white
Shaula	B	blue-white
Castor	A	white
Bellatrix	B	blue-white

release little energy but, as the star continues to contract under the weight of its accumulating outer layers, the atoms of the core are pressed closer together and fuse more and more frequently. Eventually they are producing exactly enough outpushing energy to counteract the star's inpulling gravitation. At that point the shakedown is over and the star has arrived at a stable, mature state. If the star is a massive, highly gravitational one, its infalling has taken place fast and forcefully, and its core is extremely compressed and hot, pouring out huge amounts of fusion energy to stave off further crushing and collapse. On the other hand, if the star is a slight one, its contraction has taken place gradually and gently, and its uncrowded inner atoms need to fuse only casually and occasionally in order to offset the squeeze of gravity.

For a star of any given mass the balance between gravity and fusion leaves it at a certain point on the main-sequence graph line and there it remains for most of its life. In due course, however—after a few hundred thousand years if it is a hot, blue, massive, fast-burning star; after a few billion years if it is a mild, yellow, sun-sized, temperately burning star; or after a few hundred billion years if it is a cool, red, lightweight, slow-burning star—it consumes about 10 per cent of its original hydrogen and begins to grow overbright and abnormal. The sun is approaching this point but is not expected to reach it for another three to five billion years. The exact date is indefinite because no one knows exactly how much hydrogen the sun has left in its internal regions.

The crisis that overtakes a star when it has consumed this percentage of its hydrogen arises out of the accumulating helium ash in its core. As the ash piles up in the center, fusion continues in a bright skin around it. The ash has no internal energy source, and so it contracts under its own growing weight. In the contraction its atomic nuclei are pressed in on one another, its electrons are crushed out of their orbits and gravitational energy is released. This energy raises the temperature of the core and the extra heat steps up the tempo of the fusion reactions taking place in the skin around it. The primary proton-proton reaction, important in the sun, is not much affected by the added heat, but the secondary carbon-cycle reaction quickens rapidly, becomes dominant and is soon spending the star's patrimony in a prodigal outpouring of energy.

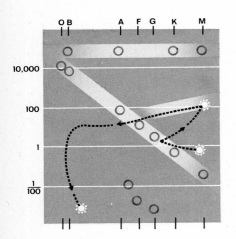

The sun's evolution, plotted on the color-brightness graph (on pages 118-119), is shown from birth to death. It coalesced five billion years ago from a gas cloud into a smallish red star, which quickly heated up to assume its present form as a yellow star on the main sequence. Here it will remain, unchanged, for another five billion years before its nuclear activities become unstable and swell it into red gianthood. This turbulent phase will quickly pass, and the sun's course will be to the left and downward on the graph, indicating a tendency to get smaller and hotter before it slides slowly toward white dwarfism.

UNDER the impact of increasing radiation from within, the star's outer regions boil vehemently and expand. The star swells and its brightness increases. But the temperature of its outer layers, pushed farther and farther from the nuclear furnaces inside, slowly falls. The puffed-up star looks red and cool. If it is many times more massive than the sun it becomes a red supergiant like Betelgeuse. If it is sun-sized or only a few per cent more massive than the sun it becomes a slightly swollen red or orange giant. If it is considerably less massive than the sun it becomes an unnamed stellar species of the future, undoubtedly larger, ruddier and brighter than it was before, but without known examples because the rank-and-file lightweight stars have not had time since the formation of the Milky Way to consume the requisite amount of hydrogen and start swelling.

In its overbright, abnormal state a star consumes its hydrogen at a dizzying pace. Nonburning helium piles up in its core more and more rapidly. Every additional bit of ash increases the gravitational squeeze on the core and increases the temperature needed to withstand the squeeze. The rising heat, in turn, steps up the rate both of fusion and of ash production. This red-giant phase of a star's life can last for only so long, and then the star will begin to turn blue again.

What happens to an average sun-sized star is that, after 40 per cent of the hydrogen has been consumed in the core, the core contracts, producing temperatures of some 200 million degrees F.—at which point the helium ceases to be inert ash and becomes lively fuel. Any three helium atoms can then merge explosively to become a carbon atom, a fourth can be added to make oxygen and a fifth can be added to make neon. In combination all these reactions generate gamma-ray energy, transforming the star's core from evenly heated, inert supercrushed gas into active vibrant gas, hotter at the center where the new reactions are occurring than in the skin where normal fusion is occurring.

THIS is a critically unstable moment in a star's life and brings on a sort of explosion known as the helium flash, or popping of the core. Calculating what it does to a star is so difficult and involves so many possibilities that the exact mathematics of stellar evolution beyond this point have yet to be worked out. Rough approximations indicate that the pop should come close to ripping a star to pieces—but not quite. The star's enormous outer blanket of gases should be able to absorb the shock, and the star—its troublesome core partly or completely dispersed into the layers around it—should seem rejuvenated and grow abruptly hotter, bluer and smaller. What happens next has been figured out only in a rough way. Being heavier than hydrogen, the ash elements thought to have been distributed throughout the star by the first popping of the core probably sink toward its center again and form a new core. But this time the core should be two-ply, with oxygen, carbon and neon predominating in its innermost regions and helium predominating in the next shell outward. Surrounding the helium, in turn, there should be a bright, normal skin of fusing hydrogen. In effect, the star should now be burning on two levels at the same time: one where hydrogen is becoming helium and another, below it, where helium is becoming oxygen, carbon and neon.

This may not be the end of internal troubles for the star. The elements oxygen, carbon and neon are all heavier than helium, and they in turn probably collect at the center in the form of a heavier, more inert ash of their own. However, if the star is large enough, and consequently if enough heat is generated through the squeeze of gravitational pressures, the neon core will pop just as the helium core did. It takes temperatures of about 1.4 billion degrees F. to activate neon ash, at which point it starts producing a still heavier ash of magnesium atoms. At about 2.7 billion degrees aluminum, silicon, sulphur, phosphorus and other atoms should begin to form. At nearly four billion degrees these elements, in turn, should be transmuted into still heavier ones: titanium, chromium, manganese, iron, cobalt, nickel, copper and zinc. Thus, it is possible to conceive of a very massive star having a series of concentric reactions taking place simultaneously, each supplying ash for a hotter one going on inside it. Presumably the kindling of each new nuclear reaction or the popping of each new core follows more and more swiftly on the heels of the one before it, making each successive stage that much shorter and the star-type that corresponds to it that much rarer.

Both theory and observation indicate that a red giant which has popped its core is headed for white dwarfdom fast. A star of the sun's mass has no difficulty getting there. Astronomers do not yet know the details of dwarfdom but the general picture is clear: a star consumes the rest of its spendable nuclear energy and, when that is gone, it contracts under its gravitational pressure until the atomic nuclei resist further contraction. After that the star, now a white dwarf, simply cools off for billions of years until it is as heatless as outer space.

Stars only 50 per cent more massive than the sun cannot achieve the quietude of white dwarfdom as easily as small stars can. The reason they cannot involves one of the strangest basic prohibitions in all nature: a mass of totally inert gas more than 1.4 times as massive as the sun cannot exist because, if it did, it would possess so much gravitational strength that it would crush even the nuclei of the atoms in it and would go on contracting forever—to a sun-sized sphere, an earth-sized sphere, a pea-sized sphere, a point-sized sphere, an atom-sized sphere, even an electron-sized sphere. As if to avoid this bizarre, impossible state of affairs, all the white dwarfs of known mass are well below the so-called "Chandrasekhar limit" of 1.4 solar masses.

Evidently, then, massive stars must have ways of shedding their excess matter before they can die. At birth they range all the way from the Chandrasekhar limit of 1.4 solar masses up to at least 40 solar masses—which leaves a lot of weight to get rid of. Although the lives of such rare massive stars are shrouded in mystery, most of them are fast spinners and can probably cut down their bulk over the eons simply by hurling off matter into space from their whirling equators. A certain number of massive stars, however, are born spinning slowly and for them astrophysicists have worked out a beautiful theory that also explains one of the most dramatic observed phenomena in the entire heavens.

WHEN the helium flash comes and the core pops in a massive slow-spinning star, the explosion is likely to be kept tamped in its place by the overwhelming force of the star's gravity. The same is probably true of the popping of the carbon-oxygen-neon core, the magnesium core, the silicon-aluminum-sulphur core and the core of heavy metals which form in succession later. Eventually a slow-spinner should be burning on seven well-separated layers, enclosing one another like the skins of an onion and progressing in steps from light hydrogen on the outside to heavy iron in the deep interior.

At this point the big, quiet star hangs in its heavens like a grenade with the pin pulled. The nuclear reaction which creates iron at about four billion degrees F. releases an inordinate amount of energy in the form of neutrinos. Just as they do from the furnace of the sun, the neutrinos must escape from the star unstoppably and irretrievably into space. But in the big star, unlike the sun, this neutrino loss is vast and deadly important. The star must shrink to fill in for the loss and the shrinkage must cause more central heating. The core temperature must rocket to eight or 10 billion degrees in a matter of weeks. Then, suddenly and catastrophically, everything must collapse. At about 12 billion degrees F., the build-up from light to heavy elements is suddenly reversed. Iron and the others break down into helium nuclei and, in so doing, absorb energy instead of releasing it. A star with such an internal temperature is, in effect, suddenly called on to repay all the energy it has poured forth munificently over the eons before. The outcome for the star is abrupt deflation, as if it were a pricked balloon. All its outer skins, reaction zones and atmospheric envelopes rush inward under the terrific, uncompensated force of its gravity. In their falling the outer hydrogen-burning, helium-burning and oxygen-burning layers are all jammed together and in a moment the remaining nuclear energy in the star is released at once, on a scale so vast and peremptory that the outside of the star explodes in a bombastic bombburst of uncountable megatons.

Stars actually do blow up with all the titanic force that theory suggests for slow-burning heavyweights. But such big stars are so scarce that their death throes are as rare as they are spectacular. Modern astronomers label them

GALACTIC CLUSTERS

Galactic clusters are loose groupings of a few hundred stars, generally found in or near the Milky Way's spiral arms. Because of their loose association, most galactic clusters break up after one or two revolutions around our galaxy's hub. The following are all visible to the naked eye:

NAME	CONSTELLATION FOUND IN	DISTANCE (LIGHT-YEARS)	AGE (YEARS)
Double	Perseus	7,340	1 million
NGC 2362	Monoceros	5,410	1 million
Pleiades	Taurus	410	20 million
M 11	Scutum	5,670	60 million
Coma	Coma Berenices	260	300 million
Hyades	Taurus	130	400 million
Praesepe	Cancer	515	400 million
M 67	Cancer	2,710	5 billion

"supernovae" and have seen them only in the distant galaxies beyond the Milky Way. On the average, a supernova goes off only once every few centuries in any one galaxy, but astronomers can see enough galaxies to witness several supernovae each year. They have found that the brightest of them hurl out almost as much light as the galaxies themselves—a single star making a final splash equal to the brilliance of hundreds of millions.

IN the Milky Way the last supernova was seen in A.D. 1604, the next-to-last in A.D. 1572 and the next-to-next-to-last in A.D. 1054. The 1054 explosion impressed and appalled Oriental astronomers of the time so greatly that they left clear records of where it was seen. Turning to that same section of the sky, in Taurus, astronomers today find the Crab nebula, a cloud of chaotic gas expanding at two and a half million miles an hour and broadcasting its turbulence in strong radio signals. At the center of the cloud is a faint blue fragment of a star lapsing fast toward white dwarfdom.

Small stellar explosions—several thousand times less forceful and more frequent than supernovae—are known simply as "novae," a word that is short for "novae stellae," or new stars. Of course these are not really new stars but, like so many things in astronomy, they were named long before they were understood and, to the early sky-watchers who saw apparently new stars blazing up out of former invisibility, the name was altogether fitting. Today a number of novae have proved on investigation to be double-star systems and there is a growing conviction that most if not all nova explosions are triggered when matter thrown off by a bloated, evolving giant strikes the surface of its white-dwarf companion.

The way stars are matched in multiple-star systems is one of the great tests of modern theories of stellar evolution. As the sun and planets probably developed out of separate whorls in a single contracting cloud of gas, so multiple stars must also have developed—two stars, three stars, four stars, many stars or many stars plus planets, all at once out of single clouds. Having been born together, the stars of any one multiple-star system should all exhibit similar aging processes. Mates of the same mass should be equally evolved. Massive stars should be more evolved than lightweight partners. Lightweight stars paired with lighter stars should not show their age at all, any more than the sun does. Some seemingly mismatched systems like the Dog Stars, Sirius and Procyon, each of which consists of normal stars coupled to white dwarfs, do not really present any problem. The white dwarfs can be explained as the fragments of massive stars which evolved fast, shed their excess mass and became cinders while their slight partners have still shown no signs of aging at all.

Though the idea may seem flamboyant and unscientific, one of the biggest blanks in the modern theory of stellar evolution is the lack of evidence of life around other stars. The primordial gas clouds have become clusters of hundreds of stars like the Hyades or Pleiades, sextuplets like Castor, identical twins like nearby Luyten 726-8, nonidentical twins like the Dog Star Sirius and its white-dwarf companion, "the Pup," and numerous other systems with unseen companions, detected only through their gravitational effects, which may be either doubles or singles, depending on whether the companions are stars or planets. No cause has yet been found as to why most stars should not have planets, born with them out of the same gas clouds by the same multiple-birth processes. And since most stars have habitable zones around them where water can be water, where gas can be held as atmosphere, and radiation received in warm-

GLOBULAR CLUSTERS

These are rarer than the galactic clusters. They are also much farther away, being found in the distant halo that surrounds the galaxy. They consist of tens of thousands of tightly packed stars. Although scientists know little about them, they are believed to be about five billion years old.

M NUMBER	NGC NUMBER	CONSTELLATION
Omega Centauri	NGC 5139	Centaurus
47 Tucanae	NGC 104	Tucanae
M 3	NGC 5272	Canes Venatici
M 5	NGC 5904	Serpens
M 13	NGC 6205	Hercules
M 15	NGC 7078	Pegasus
M 53	NGC 5024	Coma Berenices
M 92	NGC 6341	Hercules

ing wave lengths, astronomers do not doubt that life should have evolved around several million of the 100 billion stars in the Milky Way. In fact, they calculate that there should be about one site for life in every 1,500 cubic light-years.

Under the circumstances, one might expect that intelligent beings on planets around other stars, having reached the same conclusion, would try to communicate with their distant, probable coinhabitants of the galaxy. Possibly some of them are trying. Two years ago, Dr. Frank Drake of the National Radio Observatory began periodically listening for weak signals from other worlds. Except for 10 minutes of wild hope when he first tuned in his second star, Tau Ceti, and heard a clearly organized beep-beep from some still-unexplained source high in the earth's atmosphere, he had no luck. And it would be astonishing if he had. The chance is remote that either he or his successors will stumble on the right direction and frequency except after centuries of fruitless trying.

The need for trying to communicate with the creatures of other suns may seem small, but a surprising number of sane, forward-looking scientists feel that man may have to make contact with extraterrestrial brains and share technological knowledge with them if the human race is to live to a ripe old age. Modern theories of stellar evolution show that many of the faint, cool M-stars near the sun have life expectancies over a hundred billion years longer than the sun's. There, if anywhere—or so the argument goes—the descendants of the human race may enjoy their finest hours and the full fruits of biological and cultural evolution.

ALTHOUGH stellar evolution's rule of thumb is "the smaller they start, the longer they last," eventually even the smallest, most conservatively invested reserves of star stuff will be spent. In the gas clouds of the Milky Way, more stars may condense for a while but even the clouds themselves—frequently replenished up to now by the dust and gas spewed from bloated, pulsating or exploding stars—must eventually give out. If the primordial Milky Way was all hydrogen, as most astronomers believe, then the sun itself—with its supply of heavier elements—must be a second, third or even fourth generation star, born out of gas enriched long ago by the death of giant stars that were bygone almost before the galaxy took shape.

Stars that arrived still later on the scene started their lives with a smaller percentage of hydrogen than even the sun had. Eventually, all the uncommitted star stuff in the Milky Way will be so predominantly helium that the only new stars able to form out of it—assuming that conditions will permit star formation—will be massive condensations that can squeeze out a scant ration of nuclear energy from sheer force of shrinkage and weight. Later still, the Milky Way will contain no new stars at all. The globular clusters of the galaxy's halo will have disappeared long since into the darkness. In the disk, the infrared glow of a few featherweight stars, hundreds of billions of years old, will persist faintly. Then, one by one, they too will go out.

For a long time, an almost interminable time, the fading galaxy will give out a little heat as its white dwarfs cool off and turn into "black dwarfs." There are no black dwarfs in our galaxy today. Up to now, not even the most monstrous supergiants that died in the earliest eons of the Milky Way's history have had time to cool completely and lose all their energy. But, ultimately, the last expiring ghosts of white dwarfs must succumb to the chill of space. One by one they will grow as dark and cold as the voids which reach out from the Milky Way toward other, receding galaxies in the universe beyond.

STAR BIRTHPLACE, Theta Orionis, the sparkling middle "star" in the sword of Orion, turns out, in the telescope, to be much more than just a star. It is a gaseous cloud illuminated by radiation from four hot stars embedded in it. Like the area of the nearby Herbig-Haro objects *(page 142)*, the cloud is star breeding ground where astronomers hope to check out their theories that stars are born in gas clouds like this.

138

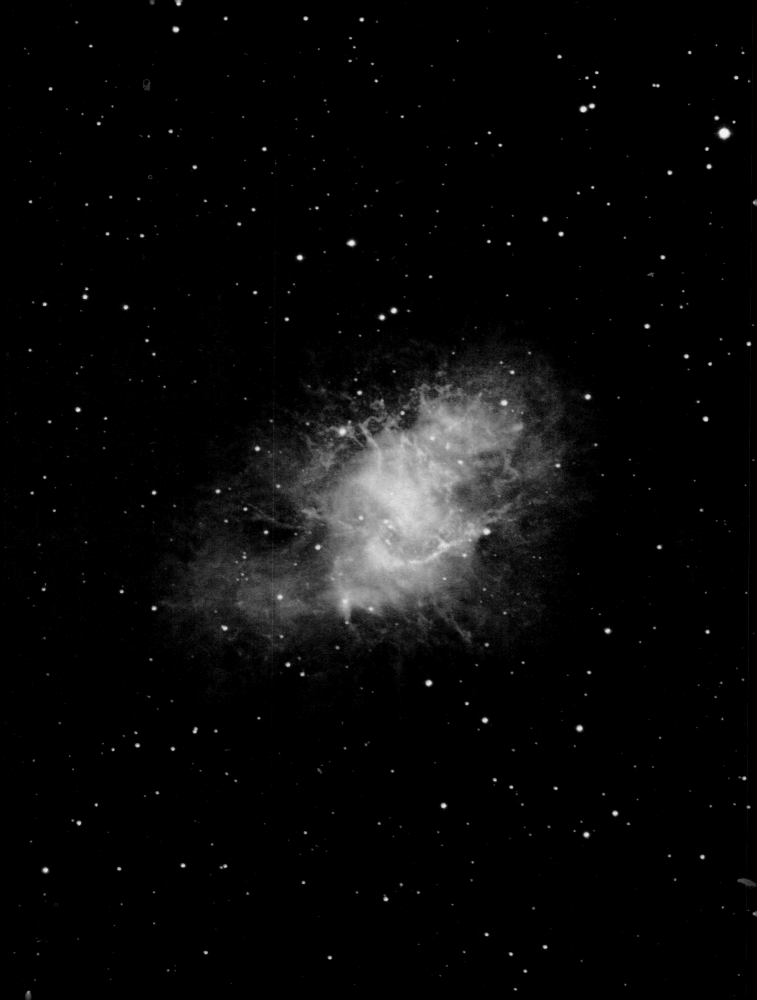

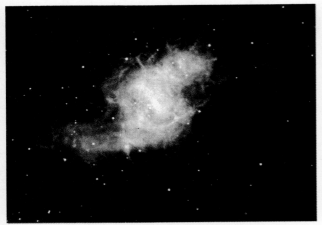

PLATE ONE: THE DISTRIBUTION OF OXYGEN

PLATE TWO: REFLECTED LIGHT OF STARS

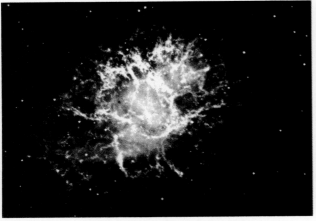

PLATE THREE: HYDROGEN IN FILAMENTS

PLATE FOUR: HIGH-VOLTAGE ELECTRONS

FOUR WAYS OF LOOKING at the Crab nebula reveal four things about it in the identification and location of its elements and light source. Special plates sensitive to particular colors and filters to block out other colors were used. Since elements emit distinctive colors, the resulting pictures, even in black and white, reveal the predominant elements present.

Tale of a Monster Star's Catastrophe

The life cycles of stars come clearer to the astronomers with almost every new set of observations. But the mechanics that produced the phenomenon on these pages were unfolded only step by step, clue by clue, over several centuries. The pictures show the Crab nebula, a vast expanding cloud of churning gas, the debris of a supernova, or monster star, explosion that was seen in the skies on July 4, 1054. For two years it burned so brightly that it shone by day, then faded, first from sight, then from memory.

In 1731 astronomers began looking through telescopes at the nebula. Bit by bit over the years they worked out a theory that this was the debris of a celestial catastrophe that had occurred some 900 years before. Proof that their theory was correct came first in 1921 when some ancient Chinese chronicles were published revealing the date of the explosion. Then in 1934 old Japanese records appeared that likened the light to that of Jupiter, which showed that this in truth was a monster star, a supernova.

RUBBLE IN THE SKY, the Crab nebula *(opposite)* shows red where atomic particles bombard its outer filaments. Its inner mass is lit by free electrons romping about its magnetic field.

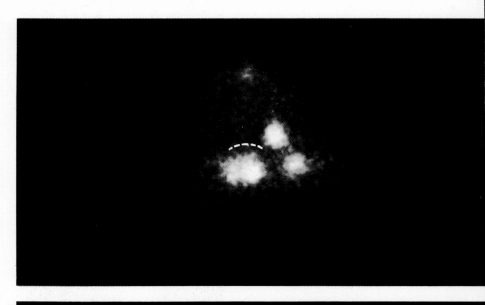

A BABY STAR
BLINKS IN

MYSTERIOUS GLOBES, called Herbig-Haro objects after the two men who first discovered them, are photographed regularly because they are thought to be stars in the making. This first picture was made in 1947.

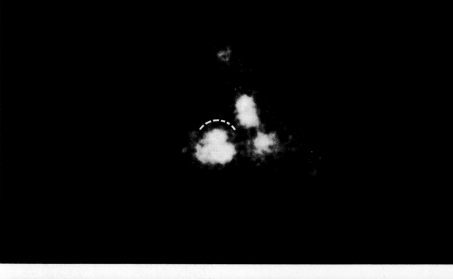

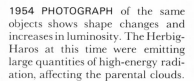

1954 PHOTOGRAPH of the same objects shows shape changes and increases in luminosity. The Herbig-Haros at this time were emitting large quantities of high-energy radiation, affecting the parental clouds.

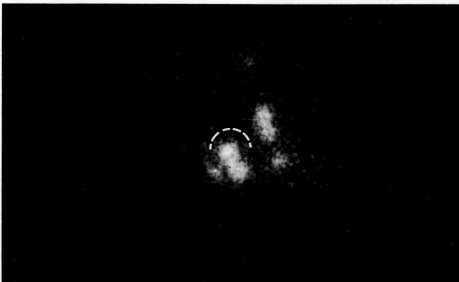

1958 PHOTOGRAPH offers another step in the evolutionary process. Scientists are not positive what is happening here but they hope they are watching the birth of T-Tauri type stars, the youngest variety known.

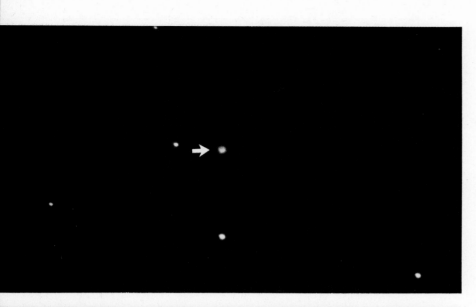

A MIGHTY STAR
BLINKS OUT

1937 PHOTOGRAPH of a far-distant galaxy reveals a supernova (see arrow) growing very bright and exploding, as did the parent of the Crab nebula *(pages 140, 141)* in 1054. This is a 20-minute exposure.

1938 PHOTOGRAPH taken a little more than a year later was exposed 45 minutes, which caused nearby stars to come up brighter. But the supernova, having released its energy, is considerably fainter in the sky.

1942 PHOTOGRAPH was exposed at nearly twice the time of the 1938 picture and over four times as long as that of 1937. All stars are much brighter and fields of luminous gas are seen. But the supernova is gone.

143

COSMIC PIONEER Edwin Hubble, in a 1949 photograph, perches in the observer's cage of the then-new, 200-inch telescope. He first discovered and studied other galaxies with the telescope's 100-inch predecessor.

7

Beyond the Milky Way

LOOKING out through the foreground confusion of the Milky Way, leaving behind the cobwebs of nearby stars and star smoke, piercing the transparent voids beyond and discovering in the dark distance the shining citadels of other galaxies—this has been the great adventure and revelation of 20th Century astronomy, an experience tantamount to seeing the beauty of the human form entire for the first time after studying nothing but the pores and hairs of a giant. To astronomers, the spectacle of the galaxies has brought new detachment and perspective, and provided many of the clues that have led to evolutionary insights. To man in general the galaxies have brought doubt and hope: doubt that all the visible universe can exist solely as a vehicle for the fulfillment of human destiny; hope that human understanding may at last come to grips with the ultimate structures and questions of the cosmos.

The sheer size and power of a galaxy can be appreciated by anyone on a clear night. One has only to look up and find a faint, moon-sized patch of brightness in the constellation Andromeda. This is a galaxy which sends light to the eye from 10 quintillion miles away. It is an object with visible size and shape, yet it is quadrillions of times more distant than any man-made satellite, trillions of times more distant than the moon, billions of times more distant than Pluto, over two million times more distant than the nearest star and over a thousand times more distant than the faintest star visible to the naked eye. Indeed, one is seeing light that left the Andromeda galaxy over two million years ago.

Being visible without a telescope, the Great nebula in Andromeda was noticed by the astronomers of antiquity and was recorded in a list of fixed "stars" by the Persian stargazer Al Sufi in A.D. 964. The only two other galaxies easily seen with the naked eye—both in the sky of the Southern Hemisphere—were first reported in Europe in the 15th Century by the Portuguese captains of Prince Henry the Navigator returning from their attempts to find a way east around Africa. Because of Magellan's longer voyage a few decades later, the two galaxies have come to be known as the Magellanic Clouds.

THROUGH the earliest telescopes the number of visible galaxies multiplied greatly, but they all continued to look as cloudlike as the Clouds of Magellan—so much so that astronomers could not tell them from actual clouds of dust and gas drifting near the sun in the Milky Way's spiral arms. Under the catchall name of "nebulae," both distant galaxies and genuine nearby clouds came to the attention of early observers mainly because they were nuisances, easy to confuse with approaching comets. One 18th Century astronomer, Charles Messier (1730-1817), who hunted comets indefatigably from the tower of the Hôtel de Cluny in the Latin Quarter of Paris, cataloged 103 of the most notorious nebulae and star clusters to remind himself to ignore them. As a result, many of the majestic galaxies near the Milky Way are identified today by "Messier," or "M," numbers, honoring a man who hated the sight of them. The great galaxy in Andromeda, for instance, is M 31.

Not only was Messier unable to distinguish between gas clouds and true galaxies, but the philosophers Emanuel Swedenborg, Thomas Wright and Immanuel Kant were similarly handicapped. However, this did not prevent them from proposing that nebulae might be "island universes," whole systems of stars so remote that their individual shafts of starlight could not be separated. The phrase was catchy and the idea quickly gained adherents, among them Sir William Herschel, who compiled the first extensive catalog of nebulae, containing 2,500 entries. Unfortunately for later students, most of the objects listed by Herschel were true nebulae, with only a few galaxies thrown in. As a result, when early spectroscopists started analyzing nebulae in the 1860s, they found that most of them were mere veils of fluorescent gas, and the island-universe hypothesis had to be tossed onto the intellectual trash heap.

Or so it seemed. But at about the same time that the best scientists had ruled out the possibility of distant galaxies, some evidence in their favor was beginning to come in. The Earl of Rosse had made out the spiral shape of M 15 in Canes Venatici and had identified 13 other spirals by 1850. The number of nebulae showing traces of spiral structure continued to grow. In 1888, when J.L.E. Dreyer published the *New General Catalogue*—which listed 8,000 nebulae by "NGC" numbers—well over half the entries were spirals. By 1908, when two new *Index Catalogues* of "IC" numbers had been added, more than 90 per cent of the 13,000 known nebulae were unrecognized galaxies.

Not that they were universally unrecognized. An otherwise unremembered scientist, Cleveland Abbe, published an article in 1867, "The Nature of the Nebulae," in which he suggested that the Magellanic Clouds and possibly other nebulae were really systems of stars similar to the Milky Way but outside of it.

It may be that many 19th and early-20th Century astronomers privately shared Abbe's conviction, but with no observational evidence to go by, few of them ventured to support island-universe ideas in print. One of the first men who had good reason to champion the idea of galaxies was G. W. Ritchey. In 1908, using a 60-inch reflector which he had built on Mount Wilson in California, Ritchey was able for the first time to resolve nearby galaxies into individual stars. Unfortunately the images of the stars were so soft and fuzzy that even Ritchey was not sure whether they were stars or tiny, remote gas clouds.

The first clear break in the observational overcast was opened up in 1912 by Miss Henrietta S. Leavitt, an assistant at Harvard Observatory. She had been set the task of studying 25 Cepheid stars in the Small Magellanic Cloud. Without any idea of the remoteness of the stars she was investigating, she noticed the characteristic that has since made these variable stars famous: the brighter they are, the more slowly they fluctuate. She thought her find peculiar and published it. At once the great Danish astronomer Ejnar Hertzsprung—codiscoverer with Princeton's H. N. Russell of the color-brightness graph and of the difference between dwarf and giant stars—realized that Miss Leavitt's curious discovery might be the key to measuring the universe.

The logic of Hertzsprung's idea is roughly as follows. The Small Magellanic Cloud is so enormously far away that, to all intents and purposes, its stars are all the same distance from the earth. This means that any differences in apparent brightness that earthly observers can detect between the various Cepheids in the Cloud reflect differences in real brightness and not merely differences in distance. It also means that the correspondence between rate of pulsation and apparent brightness must hold good for real brightness as well. Therefore, knowing the pulsation period of any Cepheid anywhere, one can at once calculate its real brightness and, by comparing this with the apparent brightness, one can always find out how far away that star is. The problem was to discover what real brightness went with each kind of pulsation period. The solution was to find a Cepheid near enough to the earth for its distance to be measured by some sure method like trigonometry. The real brightness of that Cepheid would then be known and also the real brightness of any Cepheid with the same period in the Small Magellanic Cloud. This in turn would reveal the distance to the Cloud.

Only one difficulty remained: there were not any Cepheids near the earth. Trigonometric distance measurements are reasonably exact only out to about 30 light-years, and the nearest Cepheid is 300 light-years away. As an alternative, Hertzsprung estimated the distances to a number of the nearest Cepheids by a rough-and-ready velocity method that depends on the principle that the nearer a star is the faster it should seem to move. As soon as he had amassed enough of these crude estimates, he could use the period-brightness characteristic of the Cepheids themselves to cross-check his estimates and statistically weed out error. In 1913 Hertzsprung at last calculated that any Cepheid with a period of 6.6 days had a real brightness nearly 700 times that of the sun. Cepheids were thus transformed into cosmic beacons that could be used to gauge distances wherever they were visible.

The first astronomer to use Hertzsprung's findings as a measuring rod was Harlow Shapley, later director of Harvard Observatory. Having repeated Hertzsprung's work and refined it, he went on—from 1916 to 1918—to apply the results to Cepheids in the globular clusters of the Milky Way. From his distance measurements of these stars he was able to map the Milky Way's halo, then

THE SPEED OF LIGHT

A light-year is the distance which light, moving at slightly more than 186,000 miles per second, travels in a year. Below is the arithmetic used to convert a light-year into actual miles.

```
        186,000 miles per second
                        x 60
     11,160,000 miles per minute
                        x 60
    669,600,000 miles per hour
                        x 24
      2 678 400 000
     13 392 000 00
 16,070,400,000 miles per day
                       x 365
     80 352 000 000
    964 224 000 00
   4 821 120 000 0
  5,865,696,000,000 miles per year
```

Figures of this size are obviously very cumbersome, and mathematicians use a convenient shorthand which depends on "exponents" (squares, cubes, etc.). Thus, 100 is 10^2, 1,000 is 10^3, 10,000 is 10^4. A light-year, rounded off, is about six trillion miles and is expressed as 6×10^{12}.

estimate the size of the galaxy and give the distance and direction of its hub.

In the course of their researches, Hertzprung and Shapley in effect had proved that the Milky Way is a single system of stars and that the Magellanic Clouds are remote systems outside the main bulk of it. Most astronomers, however, still failed to see in the Clouds the island universes of Kant. This is not really surprising. The Clouds are actually satellites of the Milky Way, only about one Milky Way diameter distant from it, and are not well-formed spirals but loose collections of stars and gas of the type now known as irregular galaxies.

The next major gain for the galaxies in their long wait for recognition came in 1917 when Ritchey, with his 60-inch telescope, spied a nova in a distant galaxy—NGC 6946, in Cepheus. Ritchey knew that novae normally reach a peak brightness at least 10,000 times that of the sun. But this one, even at its peak, had an apparent brightness 8,000 times *fainter* than the sun's. To be so faint, either it was no true nova or its eruption had taken place several hundred thousand light-years outside the bounds of the Milky Way. Ritchey felt sure that he knew a nova when he saw one and so, full of excitement, he looked back through the entire photographic-plate collection of Mount Wilson and found evidence of two other faint novae in supposed nebulae. Stimulated by this success, another astronomer, H. D. Curtis, reviewed plates taken with the 36-inch reflector at Lick Observatory near San Francisco and spotted three additional distant novae. Other astronomers turned up five more.

Curtis undertook to announce to the world what seemed to him unequivocal evidence that nebulae containing faint novae are separate galaxies. But the world —at least of astronomy—was not yet ready to accept the huge universe that Curtis had to offer. A historic wrangle ensued, continuing at one astronomers' conference after another from 1917 to 1924. As if to add to the excitement, the battle lines were drawn on a roughly regional basis, the pro-galaxy Californians against the anti-galaxy Easterners. In true Hollywood fashion the smooth Easterners were articulate and the Westerners were only mule-stubborn about what they knew to be right. Then, abruptly, at a conference session on January 1, 1925, the great debate ended with the reading of a communication from the California astronomer Edwin Hubble. Hubble himself was absent and word from him was eagerly awaited because he was busy taking the first "look" at the sky with the brand-new 100-inch telescope at Mount Wilson—then the world's largest. The momentous news he had to report was that the new telescope had resolved images of stars in three so-called nebulae: M 31 in Andromeda, NGC 6822 and M 33. What was more, some of the resolved stars were Cepheids, the marvelous beacons of Miss Leavitt, and they proved by their faintness and periods that all three nebulae really were galaxies far, far beyond the bourn of the island universe containing man.

Once the reality of galaxies was finally proved, the study of them shot forward as if it had been building up steam all through the previous decades of doubt and debate. Assisted by Milton Humason, one of the most technically adept observers in all astronomy, Hubble proceeded with the 100-inch to scale the ramparts of heaven. From globular clusters a few thousand light-years away he reached out to the limits of the Cepheid measuring rod, a sphere about three million light-years in radius that encompassed some 20 galaxies. From there, making rough yardsticks out of brilliant blue supergiants in the spiral arms of galaxies, he went on to chart a further sphere—containing 200 more galaxies—which is now estimated to be some 30 million light-years in radius.

Still farther out, where single stars were no longer visible, Hubble approximated distances by the average innate brilliance of whole galaxies—ones corresponding in type to those he had already studied in the 30-million-light-year sphere. With this new measure he raced on out to the then visible limits of the universe, over a billion light-years away.

In the course of this stupendous intellectual voyage—a rolling-back of human horizons unparalleled in previous history and not likely to be equaled ever again—Hubble calculated that there were almost as many galaxies outside the Milky Way as there are stars in it. His explorations were amplified and confirmed by many other astronomers, notably N. U. Mayall (now director at Kitt Peak) and C. D. Shane (director at Lick Observatory). Equally important, the knowledge of galaxies was extended into the skies of the Southern Hemisphere by Harvard Observatory astronomers under the leadership of Harlow Shapley, working at Bloemfontein, South Africa. Because of these studies, astronomers today know that throughout most of the sky, where the local river of brightness runs shallow, galaxies outnumber stars by about six to one. Some galaxies are small, some large, but on an average each of them contains over a billion stars and probably a still greater number of planets. And these systems of billions of stars continue on outward, more and more numerous with each increase in human "seeing" power, as far as modern telescopes can reach. From the faintest of them visible today, the light that reaches the earth has been in transit over five billion years—emitted about the same time that earth and sun condensed out of inchoate gas.

T HE millions of island universes discovered by Hubble are not all alike either in size, shape or orientation. In size most of them are smaller than the Milky Way, and a few are larger. In shape they vary from ragged, featureless clouds of brilliance to perfect, star-bejeweled orbs. They hang in space at all angles. Some present themselves edge on, some fullface and some in three-quarter perspective. After allowing for these differences of presentation, Hubble was able to classify the galaxies by shape and reduce their seeming diversity to a simple scheme. He distinguished three main families; spirals, or "S's," accounting for about 80 per cent of all galaxies that he knew about; ellipticals, or "E's," making up about 17 per cent; and irregulars, or "Irr's," amounting to less than three per cent. The S's looked like immense whirlpools of fire. The E's appeared more tranquil—like great luminous beach balls, flattened sometimes, as if invisible cosmic bathers sat on them. The Irr's seemed like plain globs—lumps of starplasm oozing thick and thin within formless boundaries.

Structurally, the most highly organized kind of galaxy is a spiral like the Milky Way or M 31 in Andromeda. It usually has three well-defined parts: a central hub, a halo of stars and star clusters surrounding the hub spherically, and a disk marked with spiral arms, surrounding the hub equatorially. Some spirals have a further complication: the hub is not spherical but cigar-shaped, trailing spiral arms from both ends like sparks from a blazing baton. No one yet understands exactly how these "barred spirals" (SB's) rotate or hold together. In comparison to spirals, elliptical galaxies are simple affairs consisting of just two parts: central hubs and surrounding halos. They may be more or less flattened, and their hubs may be more or less densely packed with stars, depending on how massively gravitational they are. Irregulars are vaguer still: sometimes they seem to have a trace of a central hub, sometimes haloish globular clusters, sometimes a slight discoidal flattening, sometimes even an armlike

THREE TYPES OF GALAXIES

Irregular galaxies have ill-defined shapes with occasional hints of spiral structure. They contain principally big hot blue and blue-white new stars, called Population I stars. These galaxies also have an abundant amount of interstellar dust and gas.

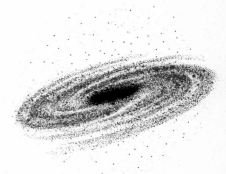

Spiral galaxies contain Population I stars in their spiral arms, where many are still forming, and older, Population II stars —red giants, dwarfs and some variables —in their tightly packed nuclei as well as in the big halo surrounding the galaxy.

Elliptical galaxies do not produce new stars since all the dust and gas has already been used up. These generally large galaxies are made up entirely of older, Population II stars consisting of big red giants, white dwarfs and variable stars.

string of blue stars and gas. But by and large they are chaotic and featureless.

Hubble further subdivided the three families of galaxies and ranged them into one continuous sequence according to their apparent disorganization and turbulence. At the placid end of the sequence he put the most perfectly spherical ellipticals and called them E-zeros. The rest of the ellipticals he arranged by their flattening from nearly spherical E1's to extremely saucer-shaped E7's. In the medium-neat, medium-calm category he threw the spirals and barred spirals, ranging from tightly wound Sa spirals and SBa barred spirals, through Sb's and SBb's to loosely wound Sc's and SBc's. In the final slot he put the structureless irregulars.

Although Hubble's barrier-shattering ascent to knowledge in the late '20s had not ended in a crash, it left almost as much debris to tidy up as the soaring stock market did in the same period. Not that any of Hubble's measurements was individually wrong—he was an extremely careful, sagacious observer —but they piled up on one another until their cumulative margins of error grew too large for usefulness. The Cepheid-distance foundations laid down by Hertzprung and Shapley had never been triple-checked for irregularities. The absorption of light by interstellar dust had never been sufficiently allowed for. In some galaxies, brilliant gas clouds had been mistaken by Hubble for single stars and equated with single stars in brightness.

Hubble himself was aware of these difficulties, just as he was aware of the limitations imposed by equipment and methods. Two of the curious anomalies he had noticed had to do with the great galaxy in Andromeda, M 31: its hub could not be resolved into individual stars, and its globular clusters seemed innately about four times as faint as the Milky Way's globular clusters. Both facts suggested either that M 31 was basically different from the Milky Way or that it was really several times farther away than the Cepheids in it indicated. Finally Hubble's colleague Walter Baade decided to investigate these puzzles and made a detailed study of the Andromeda galaxy.

During the winter of 1941-1942, when Los Angeles was blacked out by World War II and observing conditions were at their best, Baade turned the Mount Wilson 100-inch on M 31 again and again, trying by every photographic trick he knew to coax individual star images out of the galaxy's central hub. One night, in desperation, he abandoned normal, blue-sensitive photographic plates —the kind that earlier had revealed stars in this galaxy's spiral arms—and tried some new, red-sensitive plates. When he developed them, he found to his astonishment that the hub had been fractured into countless red stars. "As I turned the telescope to other regions of the Nebula," he recalled later, "moving from the center outward, the pattern of prominent stars changed from red giants between the spiral arms to blue supergiants in the arms. It looked as though the central area and the regions between the arms were populated by one kind of star, whereas another kind predominated in the arms themselves."

Baade's discovery that hub stars and spiral-arm stars are different had so many implications that it took more than a decade—and the power of the new, 200-inch Hale telescope—to work out all the consequences. For one thing, the Cepheids in the two populations proved to be different. The variable stars in the globular clusters of the Milky Way's halo, which Shapley had used as distance indicators, were ancient middle-sized ones—reaching the decrepitude of Cepheidism with far less brilliance than their younger, brighter counterparts in the spiral arms. But it was this brighter breed that Hubble had found first in

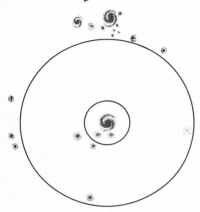

Our celestial neighborhood is remarkably empty, but it does contain a scattering of galaxies known as the Local Group. In this diagram our galaxy is at the center, with the two Magellanic Clouds directly below it. That is all that exists within 300,000 light-years of us (small circle). But at the edge of a larger circle (1,700,-000 light-years) we encounter other members of the Local Group, notably the great spiral in Andromeda (top). In this drawing, as in the one opposite, the dots and spirals are greatly exaggerated in scale.

the arms of the Andromeda galaxy; and, thinking them as innately dim as Shapley's Milky Way variables, he had hugely underrated their remoteness. That was why the globular clusters of M 31 had seemed fainter than their opposite numbers in the Milky Way. They were not really fainter—instead, this galaxy was over twice as far away as anyone had imagined. And so were all the other galaxies in which Hubble had used Cepheids as distance indicators. Baade had effectively doubled the size of the known universe.

For understanding galaxies, Baade found that the two-population concept was a master key. He restudied the 20-odd nearby galaxies within three million light-years of the Milky Way—the so-called Local Group of galaxies that hangs together by gravitation—and saw that elliptical galaxies consist almost entirely of an ancient halo population. For instance, in M 31's two small satellite ellipticals, NGC 205 and NGC 221 in Andromeda, the brightest stars are all red giants. There are no new blue stars and there is not much dust or gas out of which new stars could condense. Spirals like M 31 or the Milky Way, on the other hand, contain both halo and arm populations and varying amounts of free dust and gas. In the most tightly wound spirals there is almost no uncondensed star stuff. In flat, sprawling Sc spirals like the beautiful Whirlpool galaxy, M 51, there is a great deal. In irregulars like NGC 4449, red halo stars are scarce, blue arm stars are plentiful and potential star stuff may sometimes outweigh the lighted stars themselves.

From Baade's restudy of galactic types in the light of stellar evolution arose the idea that irregulars might represent the first stage in the development of galaxies—huge hydrogen clouds full of turbulence as they contract gravitationally and begin to condense into stars. For example, the nearest irregulars —the Magellanic Clouds—show signs of having small nuclei. The Large Magellanic Cloud even seems to have a little early spiral-arm structure. If the various forms of galaxies can be taken to represent evolutionary steps, then the Large Cloud—and other irregulars—may eventually evolve into small spiral galaxies.

How would such evolutionary changes in shape take place? There are a few tentative hints. In our own galaxy, for example, radio astronomers have found that gigantic clouds of hydrogen appear to be moving outward from the hub of the Milky Way. But what combination of rotational, gravitational and other forces could form such gas clouds into spiral arms and then hold them in a more or less stable pattern is still very much in doubt.

In any case, as the gases from a spiral galaxy's hub were used up, their outward flow presumably would slow down. Little by little the gassy part of the spiral arms might then be wound inward tighter and tighter. Stars that had formed out of the gas would be left behind in their orbits, but the free gas that remained would presumably fall back into the hub and be consumed there. Following a sequence of this sort, the galaxy would have ceased to be a spiral and would have become a highly flattened elliptical instead. Galaxies that appear to be in a condition halfway between spiral and elliptical can actually be seen. They are called S0's and they have well-developed disks, but no spiral arms in the disks and little or no dust and gas.

In elliptical galaxies, apparently, star formation has ceased. If these galaxies ever contained clouds of interstellar matter in the first place, these have been almost entirely used up. In some ellipticals dark streaks have been observed across the central regions, indicating that remnants of such raw material may still exist. But if all such vestiges of uncommitted matter were to condense

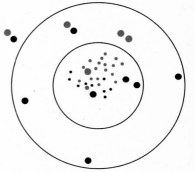

Deeper in space the emptiness increases. Each dot in this drawing is a group of galaxies, and the black dot in the center represents the entire drawing on the opposite page. The inner circle is 200 million light-years away, the outer one 400 million light-years away. Each small dot represents a group consisting of fewer than 50 galaxies; each large dot a group of 50 or more galaxies. In both drawings galaxies or groups visible to the north of the Milky Way are shown in blue, those visible to the south are shown in black.

into stars and all the most massive stars of the disk were to die, a once flat-appearing elliptical galaxy would automatically take on a more spherical appearance as its halo stars were no longer outshone by those in the disk. Whether, in addition, the actual orbits of stars in ellipticals could somehow rearrange themselves into more spherical patterns is unknown. It may be that no such step is required: fast-spinning spirals might simply evolve into flat ellipticals and slow-spinners into rounded ones.

The idea that galaxies may follow such an evolutionary path—from formless irregulars into perfectly neat spherical ellipticals—is at best a tentative hypothesis. The many small difficulties of detail that lie in its way are trivial compared to one major hurdle. This hurdle is time. Is it possible for hundreds of billions of stars to organize themselves into a spherical system before most of them have burned out? No one is sure yet, but there may be a positive answer. It depends —like the answer to all the early difficulties with stellar evolution—on mass. If a galaxy is sufficiently massive to begin with and has enough self-shaping gravitational power, it might—as does a large star—evolve much more rapidly than would a lightweight galaxy and thus reach the elliptical stage with its stars still shining. Suggestively, astronomers have found that the majority of ellipticals are indeed massive systems and that most irregulars are lightweights. Under such circumstances, it seems possible that all galaxies, from the most massive, highly organized ellipticals to the least massive, least organized irregulars, may have been evolving for about the same length of time.

IN addition to E's, S's and Irr's, a number of "peculiar objects" exist in the depths of space, galaxies torn asunder or stretched out of regularity by forces beyond astronomy's present ken. Some of them, like the Whirlpool, M 51, appear to be double galaxies connected by streamers of stars thousands of light-years long. Others, like NGC 3187 and NGC 3190 in Leo, look as if they were spinning side by side and pulling wisps of stars and star stuff out of each other by long-distance magnetic interaction. Still others, like the gigantic elliptical M 87 in the Virgo cluster, have shot out titanic flares into space—jets of brightness as great in length as entire galaxies. Finally and most puzzling of all, some pairs of galaxies, like Cygnus A, look as if they had merged with one another. Their spiral or elliptical forms occupy the same place in space, they are surrounded by disembodied clumps of stars and they emit intense radio waves many million times more powerful than the emissions of a normal spiral galaxy.

No one knows what these "peculiar" galaxies are. Several of them broadcast with such huge power that a sizable fraction of the nuclear energy locked up in their matter must be going completely into the production of radio waves. At first it was thought that the peculiars were all colliding galaxies. But astrophysicists have not been able to find any way for colliding galaxies to create such power or to collide often enough to explain the peculiars' prevalence. An alternate suggestion, put forward by Geoffrey Burbidge, then at Yerkes Observatory, is that the nuclei of very ancient or very massive galaxies may eventually explode as the stars in them are crowded closer and closer together. Burbidge's idea is that the supernova of one dying star touches off a chain reaction among its dying companions, so that the whole nucleus of a galaxy becomes a slow-burning super-supernova of indescribable proportions.

Though mysterious in themselves, peculiar galaxies have enabled astronomers to extend their knowledge of the universe out beyond the normal limits of optical observation. Most of the peculiars emit such a large fraction of their energy at radio frequencies that they are far more noticeable with radio telescopes than with optical ones. Radio astronomers find their rough bearings and then let Palomar's 200-inch sight the scene of catastrophe. In this way, Palomar's astronomers have had their attention called to galaxies on the fringes of visibility that are many times farther away than the thousands of faint galaxies that crowd the field of vision in those distant reaches of space.

Ellipticals, spirals, irregulars and peculiars—as they extend outward in all directions—begin to repeat themselves. An elliptical 10 million light-years away looks much like an elliptical 100 million light-years away. One of the main reasons that astronomers pursue the galaxies out ever farther and farther with more and more powerful instruments is to measure their velocities. As far back as 1912, V. M. Slipher at Lowell Observatory in Arizona first noticed that many of the "nebulae" (as they were known then) emit reddened Doppler-shifted light—as if they must be moving away from the earth. When Hubble and Humason began to explore the universe in 1925, they quickly found that the "red shift" is a characteristic not just of some galaxies but of *all* galaxies beyond the small Local Group. They found, moreover, that the farther they looked out, the farther the spectral lines of the galaxies were shifted toward the red end of the spectrum. Inescapably they were forced to the conclusion that the more remote a galaxy is from the Milky Way the more swiftly it is flying away. Only four years after he had first proved the reality of galaxies, Hubble was able to announce that the entire visible universe—hundreds of millions of galaxies—was not stable, but was uniformly expanding in every direction.

All sorts of ideas have been tested on the famous phenomenon of the red shift in efforts to explain away the outflying of the galaxies. But all have failed. The only explanation that agrees with anything man can measure in his laboratories is that all galaxies are indeed receding from one another, except where they are held in gravitational knots like the Local Group.

In the constellation Virgo a prodigious cluster of several thousand galaxies gauged to be about 50 million light-years distant is moving away from the Milky Way at 750 miles each second. Another cluster of some 300 galaxies nestled in the bowl of the Big Dipper looks to be 650 million light-years away and is receding at 9,300 miles per second. The Corona Borealis cluster at a distance of some 940 million light-years is fleeing at 13,400 miles per second. A cluster in Boötes at about 1.7 billion light-years is hurtling outward at 24,400 miles per second. In Hydra a group of faint galaxies, thick as raisins at their distance of 2.7 billion-odd light-years, is adding a full 38,000 miles of distance between it and the Milky Way every second, receding at a fifth the speed of light.

BEYOND Hydra ordinary telescopes cannot normally see well enough to let Doppler shifts be measured. But one peculiar galaxy—known to radio astronomers as "source 3C295" and pointed out by them because of its enormous long-wave power—seemed so extraordinary that Palomar's Rudolph Minkowski took the laborious steps necessary to check on its Doppler shift. The measurement showed that it is rushing away at over a third the speed of light. The rays man intercepts from it thus would have been emitted over four billion years ago, and in the meantime it would have traveled much farther away—to a distance of some six and a half billion light-years. Even beyond this remote galaxy both optical and radio telescopes can detect still further, fainter fugitive shapes. The galaxies barely discernible at the limits of the 200-inch are thought to be receding at about two thirds the speed of light, those at the ultimate, circuit-straining limits of radio telescopes are thought to be escaping at nearly nine tenths the speed of light.

If galaxies exist which are receding at the speed of light, their rays arrive on the earth Doppler-shifted to invisibility and thus cannot be seen. It appears, therefore, that most of the universe which will ever be visible to earth-bound man is already within range of his optical and radio telescopes and that man, if he is ever going to solve the riddles of the universe, may do so soon. Hubble had high hopes of solving them in his own lifetime but he was frustrated by the imprecision of his distance measurements.

ONE might think that if his measurements of distance were inexact, the kind of cosmic expansion Hubble discovered would also be incorrect. But this does not logically follow. The distances he measured to galaxies were off by wide margins, and the greater distances accepted today may still be off—even 100 per cent off—but Doppler-shift measurements were and are highly accurate. They made and still make the expansion of the universe an observational certainty. The outstanding questions are, first, how long has the universe been expanding and, second, will it go on expanding forever? As to the first, Hubble's original distance measurements indicated that the universe had been all crammed together in a single dense cloud of matter about 1.8 billion years ago —a length of time that seemed impossibly brief because the earth itself was believed to be more than four billion years old. Today's greater distance measurements suggest that the outrushing galaxies have taken longer to get where they are—about 13 billion years. Future distance measurements may increase this estimate again, but not very greatly. Galaxies are so big that each of the nearby ones fills a measurable angle of vision. The present distance measurements allow other galaxies to agree well with the size of the Milky Way, giving them room to vary somewhat in size, but not so grossly that they make the Milky Way seem unusually dwarfed or gigantic.

In partial answer to the second question, if the universe is expanding it must be expanding uniformly, like evenly spaced dots on the surface of a balloon being blown up. Any other assumption puts the Milky Way in a special favored place at the center of the universe. Even as the facts are, the Milky Way *seems* to be the center. At each sphere of distance around it, the galaxies appear to be receding from it at equal speed as if it were the core of the primordial explosion. But from any dot on an inflating balloon the same centrality would seem to hold true. Only uniform balloon-type expansion—as if the space between galaxies were stretching and the galaxies were holding still—can give the effect of expansion without making man's world central in a way that astronomers have not admitted since the days of Copernicus.

Valid and necessary as Hubble's expansion law undoubtedly is, there are many ways of interpreting its consequences. The orthodox conclusion is that the universe and its expansion both began from a dense, inchoate state some 13 billion years ago. A rival view, backed by a brilliant, articulate group of British theorists, is that the universe is expanding without changing—constantly beginning and constantly dying as mysterious forces create new matter and new galaxies to fill in the gaps left by expansion. It may well be that no final decision between these two competing concepts will be reached until astronomers have scrutinized the rotation, magnetism and gravitation of galaxies more closely and found out how the billions of island universes came to be shaped within calculable periods of time.

IN THE WHIRLPOOL GALAXY, AS DRAWN IN 1850 BY LORD ROSSE THROUGH HIS 72-INCH TELESCOPE, SPIRAL SHAPE WAS FIRST DETECTED

Other Island Universes

After centuries of brilliant speculation and bitter debate, man has come to accept the fact that his own huge, humbling Milky Way—containing 100 billion stars—is itself only the beginning of the cosmos. Beyond it indefinitely far in all directions hang countless other systems of stars—other "Milky Ways" like the Whirlpool galaxy above, and other galaxies like those on the following pages.

ELLIPTICALS range from E0-type spheres of stars (*left*), clustered tightly toward their centers, to flying-saucer-shaped E7's (*right*), which are flattened out by rotation.

SPIRALS, seen fullface (*left*) or in profile (*right*), range from tight, big-hubbed Sa's (*top*) to loose, small-hubbed Sc's (*bottom*). The Milky Way is an intermediate Sb type.

BARRED SPIRALS' arms trail from spindle-shaped spherical hubs. Sometimes (*right*) the arms are thick, sometimes (*left*) they are fine-drawn and encircle the hub.

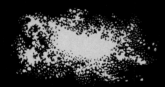

IRREGULARS are shapeless unclassifiable galaxies. Most of them contain turbulent gas clouds and brilliant blue stars, but some are poor in gas and contain old red stars.

THREE TYPES in Leo include an elliptical galaxy NGC 3193 (*left*), a normal spiral NGC 3190 (*center*) and NGC 3187, either a barred spiral or a normal spiral distorted by magnetic effects.

Do Galaxies Evolve?

Although more than a billion galaxies are visible in the range of man's telescopes, they all take one or another of the basic shapes shown at left, and the kinds of stars in them tend to fall into a crude pattern. Briefly, elliptical galaxies contain a predominance of old red stars; spirals have a mixture of old and young stars; irregulars consist mostly of young blue stars. This suggests that galaxies themselves may be evolving, with the irregulars representing youth, and the ellipticals representing old age. This is a persuasive idea, but there are puzzling aspects to the ages of galaxies which, for the moment at least, cannot be answered simply by observing the ages of the stars in them. For one thing, since it is thought that all galaxies began at the same time, why do some now look old and others young?

Some astronomers suggest that the size, density and rotation speed of a gas cloud determine the kind of galaxy it will become. If it is large and dense it will use up its gassy star stuff, condense quickly into stars, and age early into an elliptical. A lightweight, tenuous, disorganized cloud, on the other hand, will develop slowly and preserve part of its gas and dust for latter-day condensations. It may even be that the longest-lived, most irregular galaxies are still largely unlit—mere scatterings of newborn stars surrounded by dark, thin, blowing gas.

EDGE-ON SPIRAL known as M 104, or the Sombrero (*opposite*) looks like a version of Saturn but is really a tightly wound big-hubbed, dust-belted spiral galaxy 40 million light-years away

THE ANDROMEDA GALAXY, some two million light-years away, rides like a majestic counterweight to the Milky Way at the other end of the Local Group of galaxies. Its closely wound, dust-streaked spiral arms—seven according to the best count—glow blue with the light of young massive stars. Its hub in this exposure is burned out and white, but a pinkish overcast of old red halo stars and clusters can be seen around the hub. To the left of the hub and toward the picture's lower right hover Andromeda's two satellite elliptical galaxies, NGC 205 and NGC 221.

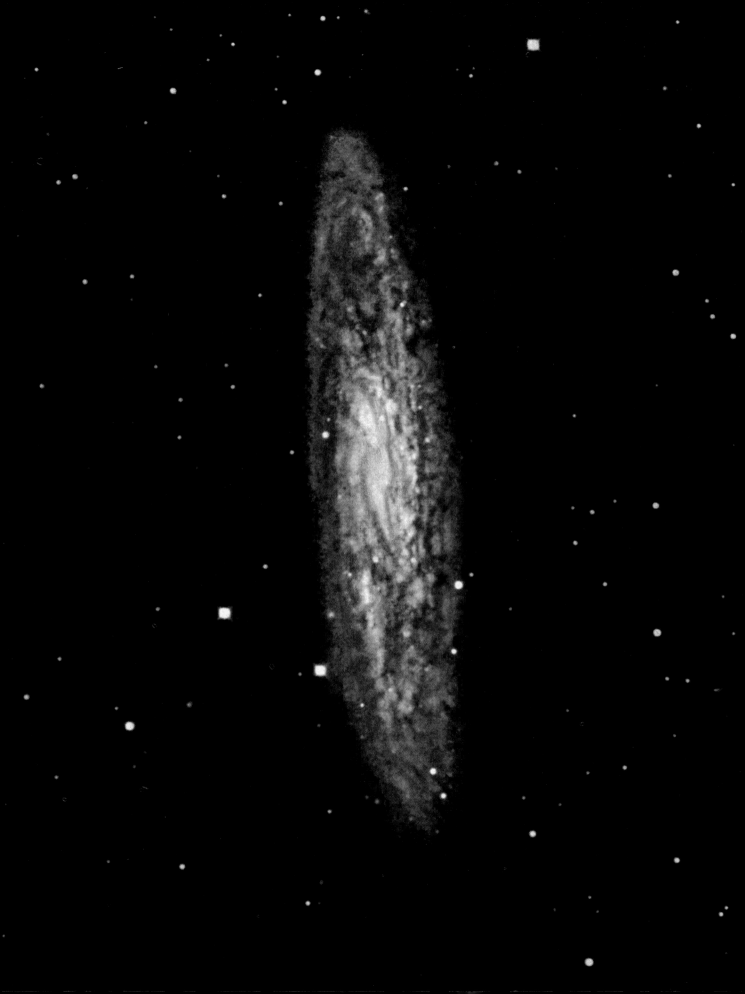

SILVERY DOLLAR of the flat Sc spiral NGC 253 lies about 13 million light-years away *(opposite)*. At such "short" distance its own speed overrides the over-all expansion of the cosmos, making it one of the few galaxies approaching the Milky Way.

BLUE PINWHEEL of M 33 whirls in Triangulum some two million light-years away. It is a small Sc spiral of the Local Group, closest of its type to earth, enabling astronomers to see clearly its many stars, including novae, supergiants and Cepheids.

THE WHIRLPOOL GALAXY, M 51, the same magnificent double system as the one drawn by Lord Rosse on page 155, reveals itself in this U.S. Naval Observatory color photograph as a sprawling Sc spiral accompanied by a small irregular companion galaxy at the right. The arms of the spiral gleam with super-giants. From between the arms, where dust and gas are scarce, comes a feeble glimmer, probably from an ancient disk-star population long unreplenished by star birth. The small companion, NGC 5195, is classed as an irregular but is one of the strange group of irregulars that are more red than blue. The big spiral

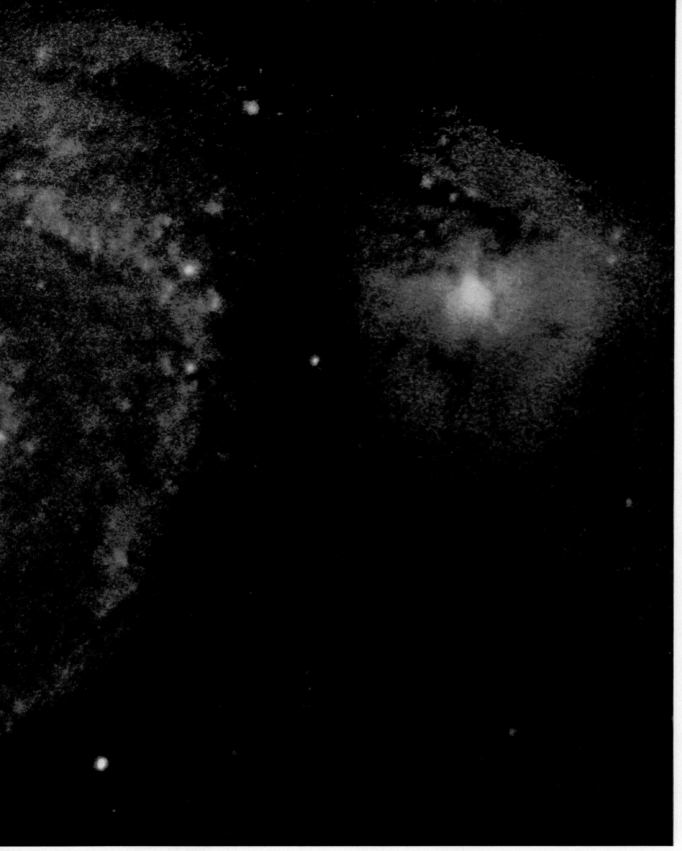

seems about to catch its companion in the coils of its huge arms, but this may be an illusion. The upper arm of the spiral actually crosses in front of the irregular. Possibly the two simply overlap in space and are really thousands of light-years apart. But astronomers generally assume that they are in contact be-cause both are receding from the Milky Way at about the same speed and must be about the same distance away—10 million light-years. Other bridges of stars and dust between galaxies are subject to the same confusion, but so many of them have been found that they are usually accepted as true interconnections.

A. Petruccelli

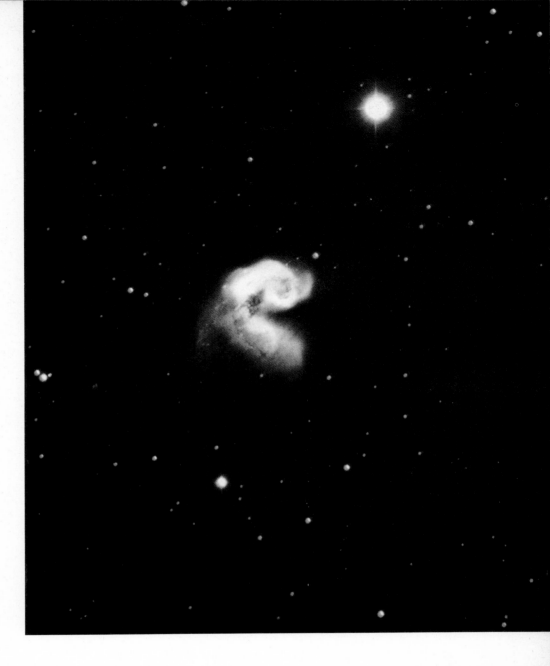

COLLISION such as might happen to galaxies in clusters is depicted by an artist (*opposite*) to show how interstellar clouds of spiral arms would interact and glow red while stars themselves would remain unaffected.

NOISY DUO of NGC 4038 and 4039 broadcasts 100 times as much radio energy as a normal galaxy. These appear to be either two galaxies colliding and distorting each other or one galaxy splitting into two parts.

When Galaxy Collides with Galaxy

Most galaxies in the expanding universe belong to groups which hang together gravitationally and resist the over-all cosmic tendency to fly apart. Some clusters, like the Milky Way's Local Group, have only a score of members, others have hundreds or even thousands. Inevitably cluster members sometimes pass close to one another and sometimes collide. It may even be that in the past the Magellanic Clouds have collided with the Milky Way. What happens in head-on encounters is not so catastrophic as one would think. The stars in galaxies are so widely spaced that they have less chance of hitting one another than do a couple of gnats flying around in the Grand Canyon. On the other hand, the gas clouds between stars must buffet one another in collisions, and must pile up in hot shock fronts like the ones depicted opposite. In their confusion they should emit red light, heat and radio waves. Some galaxies in contact with one another like the two above are indeed radio emitters and have about the right energy to be colliding. But radio galaxies are far too numerous to be explained entirely by collisions, and their radio power is far greater than could be generated by clashing gas clouds. The hypothesis of colliding galaxies is helpful but it does not solve the mystery of all cosmic din and disruption.

Six Students of Galaxies Who Shaped Our Knowledge of the Cosmos

MEASURER OF RECESSION

Milton Humason, Edwin Hubble's chief lieutenant, specialized in making long, difficult photographic exposures—up to 70 hours long—of faint galaxies' spectra *(above)*. From these he measured the recession speeds of galaxies. One of astronomy's finest technicians, he had no formal training but started life as a donkey driver. He picked up his knowledge through stopping periodically at Mount Wilson to rest his animals. Finally he persuaded the observatory staff to let him be an assistant.

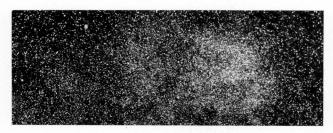

MAPPER OF THE MILKY WAY

Harlow Shapley, between 1914 and 1917, first surveyed the size and shape of the Milky Way. Since Cepheid stars fluctuate in light faster or slower depending on their innate brightness, he used them to gauge the distances of the Milky Way's globular clusters. From the arrangement of the clusters he pinpointed the direction of the galaxy's center *(above)* and estimated its distance. Later, as director of Harvard Observatory, he supervised the compilation of the Shapley-Ames catalog of galaxies.

DIVIDER OF STELLAR POPULATIONS

Walter Baade, an associate of Edwin Hubble at Mount Wilson-Palomar, turned a magnifying glass on many details of the cosmos which Hubble had skipped over. Making the first detailed study of the Andromeda galaxy in 1942, he discovered that halo and hub stars in a spiral galaxy are different in color and overall brightness from spiral-arm stars. Out of this hint he conceived the idea that halo stars might be old stars, an insight which ultimately led to modern theories about stellar evolution.

EXPLORER OF SPIRAL ARMS

Radio astronomer Jan Oort at Leiden Observatory in Holland helped map the arms of the Milky Way (*above*) by their radio emissions, thereby proving that our galaxy is a spiral. In the process Oort showed which way spiral galaxies rotate. Some astronomers had argued that spirals might be unwinding, but Oort found that in the Milky Way the arms are curved as if winding up. Oort also discovered that gas clouds are mysteriously moving from the galaxy's hub toward the outer areas.

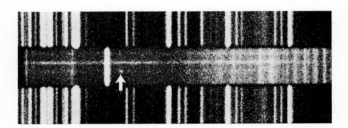

FINDER OF THE FARTHEST GALAXY

Palomar's Rudolph Minkowski succeeded Milton Humason in 1960 as measurer of the fastest receding galaxy known. With the 200-inch telescope, he tracked down a powerful source of static, 3C295, noticed by radio astronomers, and photographed its spectrum (*above*). He found that the bright ultraviolet calcium line in the spectrum had been shifted all the way to the regions of orange light—a huge 46 per cent displacement, equivalent to a recession speed of more than a third the velocity of light.

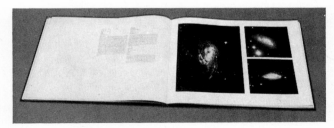

GEOGRAPHER OF GALAXIES

Palomar's Allan Sandage, at 36, is considered by many to be the successor to Hubble and Baade in deep-space astronomy. When a student, he turned up the crucial clues for clarifying Baade's ideas about stellar evolution. In the decade and a half since then he has pioneered in at least three fields: evolution of stars, evolution of galaxies and fresh observational approaches to the age, content and shape of the universe as a whole. He has also collected all Hubble's galaxy pictures in an atlas (*above*).

8

Space, Time and the Universe

EDWIN HUBBLE's discovery that the cosmos is composed of outrushing galaxies gave scientists and philosophers reason to hope that the riddles of the universe might at last be solved and the whole of creation wrapped up once and for all in a single mathematical formulation. Inspired by this hope, cosmology has developed into a modern science. Some of the best scientific minds of the century have contributed to it. Some of the liveliest controversies and rivalries of modern thought have arisen from it. And although its high goals remain unattained, they appear more attainable with each passing year.

In many ways the universe revealed by Hubble is the essence of simplicity. It is expanding like a bubbleful of hot gas suddenly released in a vacuum. Each galaxy is like a molecule in the gas. As the cloud expands, every molecule in it will double its distance from every other molecule in the same period of time. After a second period of time twice as long as the first, the doubling will take place again —and so on ad infinitum. During this *uniform* expansion, a theoretical external observer can always tell that the molecule at the center of the cloud is stationary. But an observer on the central molecule itself may not be able to tell that he is stationary. The outrushing of nearby molecules around him appears exactly the same as if he were riding a moving molecule. Only if he can see out to the edges of the cloud and count the molecules in every direction can he make sure that he is at the center of the cloud.

Since modern astronomers can detect galaxies receding at nearly nine tenths the enormous 186,000-mile-per-second speed of light and since they have not yet found any outer edge to the universe, they are convinced that the cosmos is not so simple as a mere puff of uniformly expanding gas that has partly condensed into galaxies. There are, of course, other good reasons for this conviction. For instance, if the universe were finite and had a center, and if the Milky Way were not near the center, then the total brightness of all the rest of the matter in the universe should be slightly greater on one side of the earth than the other. But the night sky beyond the Milky Way is not noticeably brighter in one direction than the other; therefore astronomers are forced to conclude that the universe extends indefinitely far in all directions. The only other possibility is that the earth is the center of everything—one planet serving as a focal point for billions of galaxies and billions of billions of other probable planets. This alternative is so preposterous that cosmologists have ruled it out from the beginning. In fact, they have made it a fundamental tenet of their creed that the Milky Way's position in the universe is not peculiar or untypical in any way. From this idea they derive a basic axiom known as the cosmological principle: namely, that the universe must be the same on the average everywhere and in all directions.

This is an extension of an even more basic principle—the uniformity of nature—that goes to the very root of all scientific thought. If nature is not the same everywhere, then the laws of science are merely local laws without universal validity. And if this is the case, man's local laws, derived in his solar system, are not applicable to the universe as a whole and man can never use them to gain an understanding of the universe. Such a defeatist attitude is not worth having, and so scientists take the position that science ultimately discovers universal laws; they believe that the universe behaves in the same way in all places; that the earth does not occupy any particularly privileged position; and that the universe has no boundaries.

SINCE the universe must be boundless and since the galaxies are receding faster and faster the farther out astronomers look, it would seem as if there must be galaxies so remote that they are fleeing outward at the speed of light. Such galaxies would never be visible because their waves of radiation would be red-shifted by an infinite amount and would be undetectable on earth. In effect, they would be beyond the cosmic horizon. Nonhuman astronomers at some halfway point would be able to see them, of course—see both them and the Milky Way—but these astronomers, in turn, would have insuperable horizons of their own. And so would astronomers in every other galaxy. Playing center to a different region of expansion, each galaxy would have a different horizon. The one common factor would be that each horizon would always take in the same-sized sample of the universe. For the universe to be understandable, the sample of it included within this cosmic horizon must be large enough to reveal the over-all cosmic structure. And once again cosmologists have reason to be optimistic. The speed of light is a fundamental constant of nature. Within the context of any one fixed frame of measurement like the solar system, light has the ultimate velocity. In cyclotrons, atomic particles accelerated to nearly the speed of light resist further pushing as if they were growing more and more massive. They act as if, upon reaching the speed of light, they would become infinitely

RELATIVITY

The theory of relativity, originally developed by Albert Einstein early in this century, has revolutionized science's concept of space, time, matter, energy, gravitation and light. Essentially, the theory demonstrates that the laws of nature are the same everywhere in the universe, and that no phenomenon can be measured by itself, but only in relation to other phenomena.

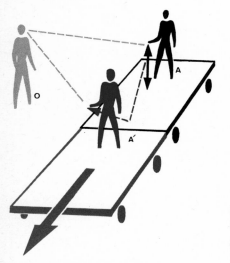

Motion and distance are relative to each other, and in measuring them time must be considered too. Observer O, at rest, sees figure A, at rest, bouncing a ball on a flatcar. The ball simply goes up and down. But if the car moves forward (blue), O sees the ball move in an arc, since A has moved in time and space to A[1]. But to A the ball still seems to move up and down.

massive—"heavier" than all the galaxies put together. In the universe, the speed of light does not limit the speed of galaxies in quite the same straightforward way. But it crops up in cosmologists' equations at critical moments—so much so that in almost every mathematical theory of the universe proposed up to now, the speed of light partly determines the over-all cosmic structure.

Since astronomers can already see out a sizable part of the way to the cosmic horizon, they feel hopeful that even with present instruments they can decide among the various "possible" universes which cosmologists have proposed. All these universes have one thing in common: although they are often very different in their implications, they do not begin to be observably different until the horizon is almost reached. This means that, in finding out which proposed universe corresponds to reality, the decisive observations are necessarily the long-range ones. And since the long-range observations of faint galaxies are the ones most fraught with error, astronomers feel that they may have to make a large number of them and find that they all agree before the real universe can confidently be separated from the various possible universes.

COSMOLOGISTS call possible universes "models." By this they do not mean balsa-and-glue models but mathematical models proceeding from basic hypotheses to systems of equations which link up such various properties as mass, energy, shape, age and so forth. Almost all present models are based, one way or another, on Einstein's two theories of relativity. Einstein's first theory, the so-called Special Theory of Relativity, came out in 1905. It evolved from a fundamental rethinking of the concepts of space and time, supported by an extraordinary discovery by the American physicist Albert Michelson in the course of an experiment he performed with light. Michelson reasoned that if a light beam were sent out in the direction of the movement of the earth, the added boost it got from the earth's own motion would speed it along a little faster than a beam sent out, say, at a right angle. As everyone knows, if a man standing on the front of a moving train throws a ball forward, the ball has not only the impetus of a man's throw but the forward motion of the train behind it. Similarly, if a ball is thrown from the rear of a train, its actual speed, relative to the earth, is much reduced. To Michelson's astonishment, the speed of light proved to be absolutely independent of the motion of the earth. No matter how carefully he measured his light beams, no matter what direction he aimed them, they all had the same speed—186,000 miles per second.

The fact that light neither loses nor gains speed from the motion of its source leads logically and inescapably to some astonishing consequences. For instance, assume that two observers flash past one another at enormous velocity and that as they pass a flare goes off between them. Since the speed of light is not affected by the speeds of either source or receiver, the light of the flare must seem to both observers to travel outward at equal speed in all directions. After an interval of time each observer, with properly rigged mirrors, can prove that he is at the center of the light's expanding sphere of brilliance. Yet by this time the observers have moved apart. How can they both possibly be at the center of the same sphere of outrushing light?

Einstein found that the only way to reconcile the different viewpoints of observers moving past, toward or away from one another at appreciable fractions of the speed of light, is to admit that their measuring instruments register distances differently, times differently and masses differently. The mass of a fast-moving object should increase—which is exactly what does happen to a particle

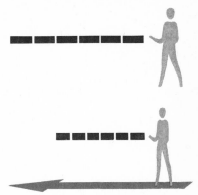

An observer and his measuring rod both are compressed in the direction of motion when approaching light's speed. The man at top, at rest, is holding a ruler with six equally spaced units. The man at bottom holds a similar ruler, but both he and it have contracted due to their great speed. Yet, in his frame of reference he obtains the same measurements as the man at top.

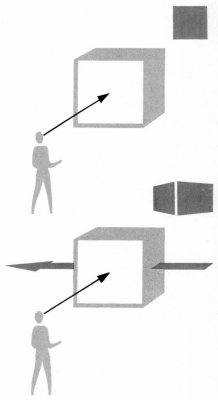

An object, too, shortens in the direction of its motion as it approaches the speed of light. At top, an observer, relatively at rest, sees only one side of a cube, also at rest. At bottom, the cube is represented as nearing the speed of light in the arrow's direction. An observer at rest would see its front end shortened and also see the second side hurrying into view a little early.

in an atom smasher. At the same time, the length of an object should shrink in the direction of its motion and its orientation should be skewed. For instance, suppose a cubical box is flashing past an observer at nearly the speed of light and in such a way that, when it has just pulled up abreast, it is seen broadside —only one of its six sides visible. According to Special Relativity, this side will seem shortened in the direction of the motion of the box; also, a little of the back side of the box will become visible before it should. The result is that the box seems to be flying along cater-cornered, presenting two faces at once, each shortened as if by perspective.

FOR a fast-moving object even the flow of time should be affected, making its clocks and atomic processes run slow. That this actually happens is again demonstrated in atomic accelerators. Unstable short-lived particles live longer if they are moving fast than they do if they are standing still or merely loafing along. They also slow down their emission of energy pulses, and this in turn increases the amount of Doppler shift in the radiation they produce. Enhanced Doppler shifts due to slow-running time have to be taken into account in interpreting the light of distant galaxies. For instance, radio galaxy 3C295 shows a Doppler shift which would normally be equivalent to a recession velocity of almost half the speed of light. But because 3C295's red shift has been enhanced by its slow time rate, Special Relativity gives its real recession velocity as little over a third the speed of light.

In Special Relativity, Einstein provided rules for relating the measurements of observers traveling at steady speed along straight lines. In General Relativity he related the measurements of observers traveling not only at steady, straight-line speed with respect to one another but also at changing speeds on curving flight paths. To do this he had to reconsider the two fundamental properties of a piece of matter: its inertia, which makes it resist changes in the direction of its motion, and its gravitational properties, which force it to change its speed and curve its path constantly in response to the presence of other matter in the universe. After pondering these properties, Einstein decided that they must be the same thing: that inertia *is* gravitation and that both arise from the effect matter has on the space in which it exists.

In Special Relativity, Einstein had had to abandon the concept of absolute space in order to accommodate the true nature of light. In General Relativity he went one step further. The presence of matter in space always creates a curved gravitational-inertial field which makes bodies form as spheres and makes satellite bodies orbit in circles or ellipses. Under the circumstances Einstein saw no merit in clinging to the abstract idea that space is laid out in straight lines and ruled by the theorems of Euclidean geometry. He saw no reason why space should have any geometrical properties except those imposed on it by the presence of matter.

Having reached such conclusions, Einstein might have gone no further if it had not been for the existence of multidimensional non-Euclidean geometry, an abstruse branch of mathematics which had been beautifully worked out by the short-lived 19th Century German genius Georg Friedrich Riemann (1826-1866). Riemann's geometry was a total generalization of ordinary geometry, extending the mathematics of curves in two dimensions and curved surfaces in three dimensions to equations that would also describe nonvisual "curved spaces" in four dimensions, curved "hyperspaces" in five dimensions, and even curved "n-spaces" in any number of dimensions. Using Riemann's geometry, Einstein was able to describe the gravitational fields around matter in such a way as to make the strange, motion-created distortions of time, length and mass discovered in Special Relativity become mere geometric properties of local space. The dimensions of height, width, depth, time and mass might vary gradually from point to point in the universe, but the variations would be simply reflections of curvature in this many-dimensional cosmic geometry. By treating the variability—the dimensionality—of the cosmos in this way, Einstein was able to rewrite the equations of physics so that they would work for all observers in all states of motion throughout the whole extent of four-dimensional space-time and even of five-dimensional space-matter-time.

Visualizing four- or five-dimensional geometries is not merely difficult: it is impossible. The logic of multidimensional volumes or spaces is clear in equations but is totally obscure in visual terms because human eyes seldom have to take in more than two-dimensional surfaces—the lay of a landscape, say, or the contours of a sofa. When faced with a truly three-dimensional visual problem such as the remoteness of a bright object in the air in front of an airplane, human perceptions falter and pilots have been known to make near-suicidal turns or dives to avoid meteors that were actually hundreds of miles in front of them.

In understanding the multidimensional cosmos, mathematicians, following blind algebraic insights, have a great advantage over untrained, "reflex" human beings. What Einstein discovered in the course of thinking about General Relativity is that space is a curved *volume* responding to the presence of matter by local three-dimensional dents in its substance. In visual terms space can be compared to a rubber sheet. Each celestial body in it is like a cannon ball making a big dent around which lesser bodies roll like marbles. This sort of denting represents local curvature in space. And its existence is proven by the fact that the light of a star—the straightest kind of line that anyone would want to think about in the universe—is bent slightly as it passes through the gravitational field of the sun. In other words, the sun by its presence curves the space around it.

IN addition to local curvature caused by individual chunks of matter, Einstein saw that the universe might have an over-all curvature. Starlight, taking the shortest route from one remote region to another and threading its way through the local gravitational fields of stars and galaxies, might end up headed a slightly different way from the way it started. Its over-all path might be a curve, either a "closed" curve coming back on itself like a circle, or an "open" curve that never comes back on itself. Then again, the small kinks in the flight path of a ray of starlight might cancel each other out so that the ray did not curve at all and space over-all was straight. Taking all these possibilities into account, Einstein decided that universal space must follow one of three mathematical patterns: it must be positively curved, negatively curved, or uncurved. Positive space curvature is like the curvature on the surface of a sphere, but with one more dimension added. Uncurved space is ordinary Euclidean space, the type one becomes used to from living in flat-walled, four-square rooms. Negatively curved space is probably the most difficult to imagine. The two-dimensional surface equivalent to it is the surface of a western saddle—but a saddle extended so that the pommel and back curve upward indefinitely and the sides curve downward indefinitely.

In any kind of curved space, light always takes the shortest path between two points. In mathematical terms, it follows a geodesic. On the surface of the earth a geodesic is a great circle, like the routes of trans-oceanic airlines. In

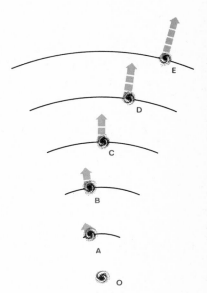

The speed of galaxies, as they recede from each other, can only be measured in relation to the stationary earth. When astronomers say that the farther away a galaxy is, the faster it seems to be moving, they are not referring to the galaxy's true speed, which is not known, but to its speed relative to an observer on earth.

In the diagram above, observer O is assumed at rest. Galaxy A seems to move away from observer O at one unit of speed, galaxy B at two units, galaxy C at three units, etc. But galaxy E, to an observer on it, would seem stationary, with all the others moving away from it, and O moving the fastest. To an observer on C, galaxies B and D would be receding at the same speed. Thus the universe appears to expand in the same fashion, no matter where the observer is standing.

positively curved space, geodesics are closed curves, like circles or ellipses. In negatively curved space they are open curves, like hyperbolas or parabolas. In Euclidean space they are straight lines.

Since light follows geodesics, a man looking out far enough into the universe should be able to determine its curvature or noncurvature by means of the distribution of galaxies. The angle of vision of a man looking out into positively curved space is like the angle between two longitude lines reaching southward from the North Pole. At first the lines take in increasing amounts of distance just as ordinary straight lines would. But little by little the taken-in distances do not increase as fast as they should. And if the man can see beyond the equator, the taken-in distances actually begin to decrease until they reach zero at the South Pole. In the same way, each successive area taken in by looking farther and farther out into positively curved space would be smaller than the area taken in by looking out equally far into uncurved space. Moreover, the number of additional galaxies revealed in each new shell of telescopic penetration would be smaller than expected and at length the number would actually decrease. In fact, eventually the observer would be looking beyond the opposite pole of the universe and would begin to count galaxies he could see more easily by turning around and looking in the opposite direction. In a positively curved universe, an astronomer with a powerful enough telescope should even be able to look all the way around one cosmic circumference and see the back of his own head. Since light takes time to travel, however, he would really see only the site which his head might have occupied billions of years ago.

In the same way that successive spheres of observation in a positively curved universe should reveal abnormally small increases in areas and in numbers of galaxies, so in a negatively curved, western-saddle type of universe each successive sphere should show an overincrease in area and an overabundance of galaxies. The geometric principle at work can easily be appreciated by squashing a negatively curved saddle and a positively curved skullcap into flat planes. In the process the saddle bunches up in folds because it has more area than a plane, while the skullcap tears apart because it has less area than a plane.

THROUGHOUT the 1930s Hubble tried to determine the curvature of the cosmos by counting the number of galaxies at each successive sphere of faintness. He failed because his estimate of distances was inaccurate and because, in any case, the galaxy-counting method does not reveal pronounced curvature unless it is carried out almost all the way to the ultimate cosmic horizon. Working over Einstein's equations, Caltech's H. P. Robertson, and more recently Palomar's Allan Sandage have developed an observational method to determine the curvature or noncurvature of the universe. As the universe has expanded, it must have braked itself as the mutual gravitation of galaxies acted to slow their flights one away from another. In a positively curved universe in which space curves in on itself, the braking would be more effective than it would be in either a "flat," Euclidean universe or a negatively curved, western-saddle type of universe. The measure of the braking effect is the speed of expansion in the past. If the speed of expansion was much greater in the past than it is now, then the universe has been braked a great deal and its curvature is positive. If it has been braked only a little, its curvature may be zero. If it has been braked hardly at all, its curvature is negative.

Amazingly enough, the amount of braking that has taken place in the past is something that can be observed in the present. This is because man, looking

THE CREATION: THREE THEORIES

The creation of the universe is currently explained by three different theories. All three agree on one essential point: it is expanding, because most of the galaxies man can see are receding from each other. This observable fact, and the widely held belief that stars have different ages, is taken into consideration by each of the major theories of the universe's origin.

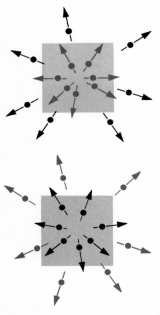

The "steady state" theory argues that the universe has always been expanding at a constant rate (top) and that new matter is constantly being created. Consequently, there is always the same amount of matter in a given space (bottom). There never was a "big bang" according to this theory, and the galaxies will never return to a hypothetical center of the universe.

out into the universe, is also looking back into the past. Near the limits of vision with Palomar's 200-inch, for instance, galaxies are seen in light that left them over five billion years ago, when they were over five billion light-years away. The amount of Doppler shift in their light shows how fast they were receding then, and the brightness of their light shows how far distant they were. In a uniformly expanding universe, galaxies at that distance should be scurrying outward at a certain definite velocity, but the light from the past shows these galaxies to have been receding faster than that. Their surplus velocity thus reveals the amount by which gravitation has since braked the expansion of the universe. By inserting this amount of braking into Einstein's equations, an astronomer can determine what kind of curvature the expanding universe has.

Up to now the few laborious, error-fraught soundings that have been made on the light of faint, fast-receding galaxies indicate that the universe is probably positively curved. This means that the universe may be unbounded but finite—it may extend indefinitely far in all directions without being infinite in mass. Looking out from any galaxy, a human or other intelligent being should see along a closed light path curving in on itself in space and simultaneously bending back through time to the very beginning of expansion. Because of the curvature, every galaxy is surrounded by the universe evenly and indefinitely on all sides without the universe being infinite. In the same way, every point on the earth is surrounded evenly and indefinitely in all directions by the surface of the earth without the earth being infinitely large.

Stranger still, a positively curved universe, responding only to gravity, can oscillate. Assuming that its total mass is above a critical value, the universe's expansion will eventually be braked completely and come to a stop. After unimaginable lengths of time, probably far more than the burning-out of the last stars in the galaxies, the universe would start contracting again. After more billions of years the contracting universe would reach a superdense, superhot state, all matter would be dissolved again into a gas of elemental protons and neutrons and the universe would start expanding again—to repeat its cycle and go on expanding and contracting indefinitely like a beating heart or a sighing lung.

On the other hand, the early measurements that imply a positively curved universe may be wrong. Instead, the universe may be negatively curved, or not curved at all. In either of these cases it should go on expanding forever, the galaxies moving farther apart as they burn out, until nothing is left but an infinitely diffuse dust of dark cinder-galaxies spread uniformly thin over everywhere and forever.

A further possibility has been proposed and backed articulately by a school of British cosmologists—notably Fred Hoyle of Cambridge, Hermann Bondi of the University of London and Thomas Gold, who is currently at Cornell. They propose that the universe is roughly the same not only every*where* but at every *time* as well. They call this culmination of the Copernican ideal—which makes man's view as typical and ordinary throughout the course of time as it is throughout the extent of space—the perfect cosmological principle. To keep the universe in such a "steady state," new matter or energy has to be continuously created at a rate equal to the mass of one hydrogen atom in each quart of space every 500 billion years. Anti-steady-state cosmologists object to this feature because scientifically there is no evidence that mass-energy can be created. On the contrary, one of the cardinal laws of physics is that mass-energy is con-

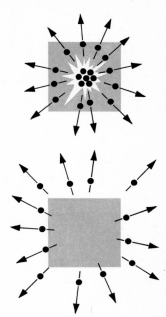

The "big bang" theory states that the universe began with a gigantic explosion (top), and that galaxies will expand indefinitely, beyond our instruments' range, instead of returning to a hypothetical center of the universe (bottom). Since this theory claims that all elements were created in the first half hour of the explosion, it assumes new matter is not being created.

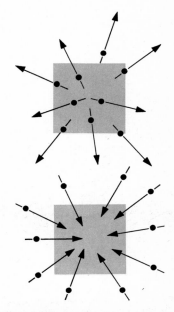

The pulsating universe theory claims that all matter is flying apart from a previously compacted mass (top). Eventually it will slow down, stop, and begin to contract under the mutual gravitational pull of its parts (bottom). Ultimately it will become so condensed that it will explode again. In the process, matter is neither created nor destroyed, merely rearranged.

served and that the quantity of mass-energy in the universe never changes, even though its distribution does.

By allowing new matter continuously to materialize in space, the steady-state school can let normal physical laws do the rest. The new matter creates pressure which forces the universe to expand constantly. The new matter then condenses into galaxies and fills in the voids left by the very expansion it causes. The space in which the expansion takes place is of the ordinary flat, Euclidean kind and the amount of matter in it is infinite and steadily growing more infinite. Because space is flat and infinite, galaxies are flying apart not only faster than the speed of light but at infinite speed. Their number is infinite and, of course, time is also infinite.

Because steady-statism makes a great number of flat, unambiguous statements about the universe, and because it does not lead to the conclusion that the universe began 13 billion-odd years ago in a superdense condition that obliterated all traces of any previous state, many scientists find it attractive. Because the theory demands that something be created out of nothing and that the universe grow ever more large and infinite without ever having to pay back its increase in mass-energy, many other scientists find it unattractive. Some of them even say that it is pure pipe dream. The greatest count against it, however, is that it predicts no slowing-down of expansion over the course of time. Since the best measurements to date on distant galaxies do indicate such a slowing-down, steady-statism is probably one possible universe that will turn out to be impossible.

For the present, then, the one possible universe best supported by evidence from the real universe is the positively curved, oscillating model. But even this one does not completely jibe with reality. The greatest discrepancy is time. Crude, unadjusted measurements of cosmic expansion indicate a beginning some 13 billion years ago. But if the universe has been braking itself and is positively curved, it must actually have started expanding only seven or eight billion years ago. By contrast, the oldest stars in the Milky Way—according to some modern theories of stellar evolution—may be as much as 15 or 20 billion years old. And some galaxies look as if they should be older still. A tremendous amount of work still needs to be done on the evolution of stars and galaxies before astronomers can know whether the galaxies on the dim horizons are only as far away as they seem or whether, when they emitted their light billions of years ago, they were really far brighter than normal galaxies today and thus much farther away than they look.

From the standpoint of the human race, all the possible universes that cosmologists have proposed so far are bleak. Man may eventually gain a fuller or even a full knowledge of the universe from observatories on the smogless, airless moon. His distant descendants may conceivably survive the fiery expansion of the sun five or six billion years from now. Some of them may even migrate to the planets of other stars in the Milky Way, but migrating farther, to other galaxies, seems definitely impossible. Even if a man could saddle a light ray and be off, he would have to journey over two million years merely to reach the nearby Andromeda galaxy. Eventually, then, when the smallest stars of the Milky Way wink out, life as we know it must be extinguished. Afterward, for whatever comfort the thought may bring, it is conceivable that the universe will contract and be reborn from a new, hyperdense state and that other earths and other intelligent creatures will evolve again—and again—and again.

EINSTEIN'S STUDY IN PRINCETON, NEW JERSEY, SHOWN SHORTLY AFTER HIS DEATH, PLAINLY BESPEAKS UNFINISHED COSMIC BUSINESS

The Ultimate Questions

When Albert Einstein died in 1955, his marvelous brain had created much of the mathematical framework for understanding the microcosmic laws of the atom and the macrocosmic laws of the universe. At his death he was trying to synthesize the two in one set of equations, one "Unified Field Theory." This problem still remains unsolved—as do other cosmic questions posed on the following pages.

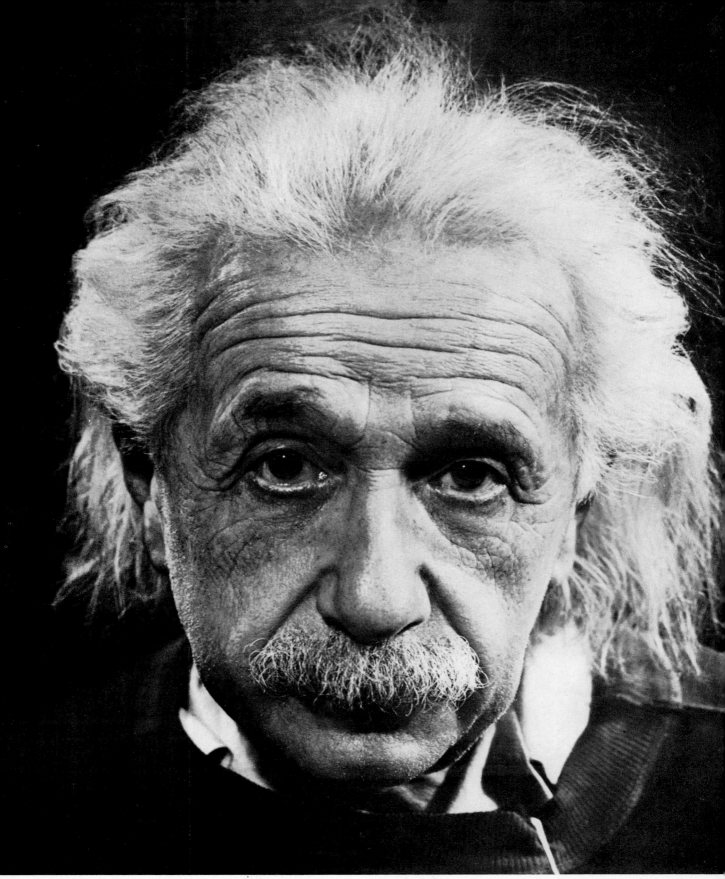

MASTER COSMOLOGIST Albert Einstein, whose relativity theories revolutionized both atomic and cosmic thought, has a look of farseeing abstraction in this 1947 picture. A decade before Hubble found the cosmos to be expanding, Einstein's equations showed that it should be either expanding or contracting. Unable to believe his own results, he rewrote them to let it stay static.

THREE KINDS OF SPACE possible in relativity are akin to these two-dimensional surfaces. The plane *(left)* represents flat Euclidean space where light rays travel along straight lines. The sphere represents positively curved space where light follows closed curves like circles. The saddle at right represents negatively curved space where light follows open curves like hyperbolas.

Is the Cosmos Curved? And if So, How Curved?

In 1916 Albert Einstein published his General Relativity, a mathematical theory of gravitation which replaced Newtonian concepts with abstractions so difficult that it took a decade even for most mathematicians to grasp them. The essence of Einstein's theory was that the presence of matter distorts space and makes it curve. The concept of space curvature stemmed from many-dimensional, non-straight-line geometry created abstractly through equations. Just as a surface can curve in ordinary three-dimensional space, so in non-Euclidean geometry a three-dimensional space can itself curve in four-dimensional space. No one can visualize such a curved space because man is not four-dimensional, but from a purely logical aspect it is a clear possibility.

By equating the presence of matter with space curvature, Einstein rewrote the laws of physics in non-Euclidean terms and found that in this form they made some predictions measurably different from those of Newtonian theory. According to Einstein, Mercury's nearest point to the sun should revolve around the sun slightly faster than it should by Newtonian calculations. A massive star's gravitational field should slightly reduce the energy of radiation leaving it. Starlight grazing the surface of the sun *(below)* should bend by an angle of 0°.00049. Observations have verified all three of these predictions and have proved beyond doubt that Einstein's equations describe reality better than Newton's.

General Relativity suggested that the universe as a whole is positively curved, uncurved, or negatively curved, like the analogous two-dimensional surfaces above. Which it is can only be determined by precise measurements of distant galaxies. At present these are too inexact to give any definite answer, but they indicate that the universe may be positively curved.

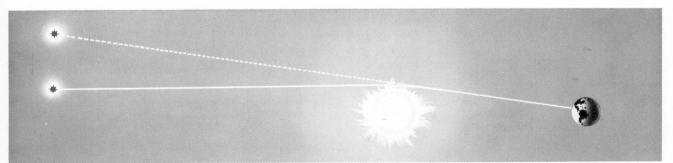

BENDING OF STARLIGHT, predicted by Einstein's General Relativity Theory and verified in 1919, occurs when a star's rays (solid line) pass through the sun's curved gravitational field. The amount of bending can be measured on the earth *(right)* by the very small angle between the star's calculated real position (lower-left symbol) and apparent position (upper-left symbol).

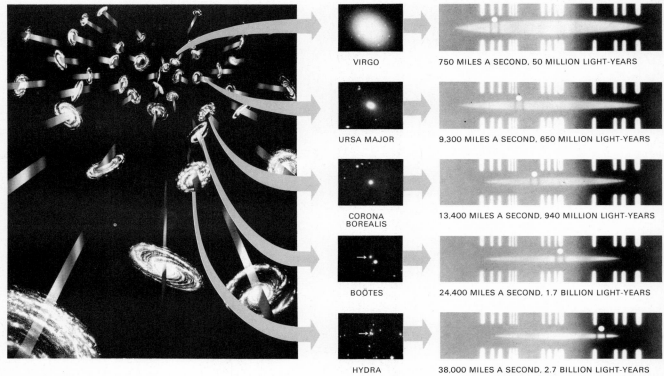

VIRGO   750 MILES A SECOND, 50 MILLION LIGHT-YEARS

URSA MAJOR   9,300 MILES A SECOND, 650 MILLION LIGHT-YEARS

CORONA BOREALIS   13,400 MILES A SECOND, 940 MILLION LIGHT-YEARS

BOÖTES   24,400 MILES A SECOND, 1.7 BILLION LIGHT-YEARS

HYDRA   38,000 MILES A SECOND, 2.7 BILLION LIGHT-YEARS

THE GREATER ITS DISTANCE from the earth, the greater the speed of a galaxy and the greater its red shift. All three elements are linked in the pictures above. At left is a reduction of the painting opposite, showing how the light of five representative galaxies shifts more to the red end of the spectrum as each recedes from a central point. Blue arrows connect the galaxies with actual photographs and spectra. The white dot over each spectrum shows how the spectral lines of calcium move with each step. The spectra of galaxies moving faster than Hydra are usually too faint to discern, one of the rare exceptions being the radio-discovered galaxy 3C295 (*pages 167 and 168*). Its spectrum resembles those of the outermost galaxies shown here.

Is the Universe Truly Expanding?

No insight of science is more meaningful than Edwin Hubble's discovery that the cosmos is expanding—vanishing outward into space like a puff of smoke. The evidence for Hubble's find is the "red shift," shown in the spectra of galaxies above. The fainter and thus farther away a galaxy is, the more its spectral lines shift toward the red end of the spectrum and the faster it must be receding from the Milky Way. No other explanation of the red shift has ever been lab-demonstrated. Moreover, relativity shows that the universe cannot remain static—unless forces beyond man's ken are at work in it.

The universe, therefore, is undoubtedly expanding. And it is expanding uniformly. A galaxy one billion light-years away recedes half as fast as one two billion light-years away. In a given time every galaxy increases its distance from every other by the same percentage. This means that from man's view the Milky Way seems to be the center of the expansion and that any other galaxy, from the view of its own inhabitants, would seem equally central. A uniformly expanding universe must look roughly the same from any place in it. But it need not look the same at every instant in time. Some cosmologists think that new galaxies materialize in the voids left by expansion and keep the universe looking the same—in a "steady state." But most think the universe is changing and becoming spread out more thinly. In the process its expansion is slowed slightly by gravitation. If space is positively curved, as the slim evidence indicates, the expansion will finally run out and contraction will set in.

THE RED SHIFT is the prime visual argument for an expanding universe. In this painting, with the Milky Way assumed to be at the center, galaxies near it are moving relatively slowly and are seen at the blue end of their spectra. The distant fast-moving ones are shown shifted to the red end of their spectra.

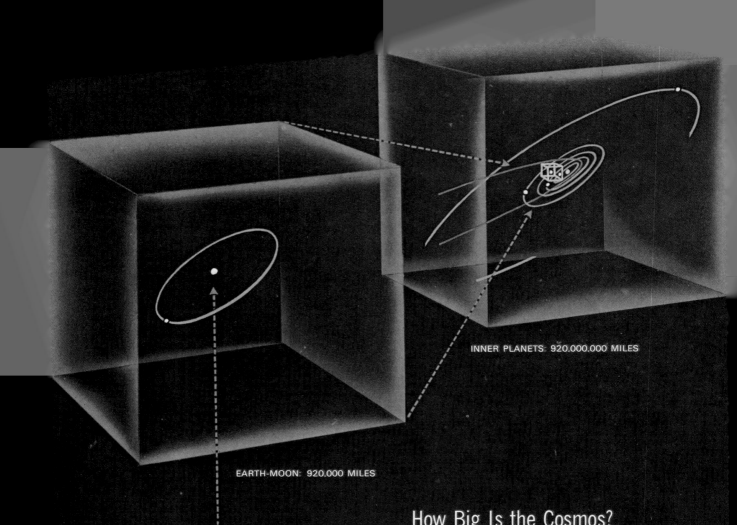

INNER PLANETS: 920,000,000 MILES

EARTH-MOON: 920,000 MILES

EARTH: 7,927 MILES

How Big Is the Cosmos?

How enormous the known cosmos is can be seen from this set of cubes. Each successive cube is a thousand times as wide and a billion times as voluminous as the one before it. The contents and width of each one are described in the caption beneath it. If they had been drawn the other way, decreasing in size from the earth-moon system *(above, left)* instead of increasing, the sixth cube would be about the size of a typhoid germ. Thus, man's perceptions operate midway between the extremes of macrocosm and microcosm.

So placed, man can make revealing measurements. If present ones are correct, he is now seeing galaxies receding at nearly half the speed of light. And if present theories are correct, the speed of light may be a limit which defines the utmost extent of the observable cosmos. Man may have a good sample of the universe within his grasp and may be able to generalize from it. By the simplest interpretation—and that best backed by the facts—the universe is finite but unbounded. A light ray may travel infinitely far, going round and round in curved space, but it moves in a cosmos with a finite radius—a radius of about 13 billion light-years.

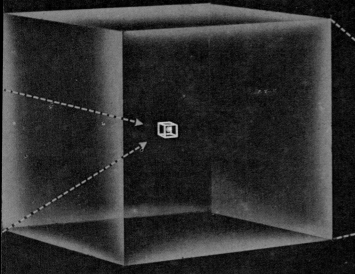

SOLAR NEIGHBORHOOD: 920,000,000,000 MILES

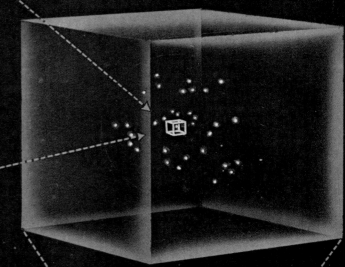

NEARBY STARS: 920,000,000,000,000 MILES

MILKY WAY: 920,000,000,000,000,000 MILES

NEARBY GALAXIES: 920,000,000,000,000,000,000,000 MILES

A SKYHOOK BALLOON LIFTS INSTRUMENTS OUT THROUGH THE EARTH'S OBSCURING AIR TOWARD SPACE, THE ARENA OF FUTURE ASTRONOMY

Can Man Find the Answers?

Confronted by cosmic subtlety and immensity and the total strangeness of such phenomena as galaxy NGC 5128 *(opposite)*, man may well despair of ever sounding the universal scheme in full depth. The largest telescopes are already pushed to their limits and earth's quivering atmosphere makes larger in-struments useless to build. The only way to extend knowledge greatly is to send instruments into space by balloons, like the one above, or by earth satellites. Eventually on the airless moon astronomers may find nearly perfect "seeing conditions" and then, perhaps, they will learn most of the answers.

ENIGMATIC GALAXY NGC 5128, 15 million light-years away, emits radio noise 1,000 times more intensely than a normal galaxy—as if most of its matter were being converted into radio energy. It could be a dusty spiral colliding with an elliptical galaxy.

Appendix

GLOSSARY

Aphelion: that point of a planet's orbit farthest from the sun.

Asteroid: a small planetlike body usually orbiting the sun between Mars and Jupiter.

Binary Stars: two stars revolving closely around each other.

Blue Shift: *see Doppler Effect.*

Cepheid: *see Pulsating Star.*

Cluster:
  Galactic: a loose group of stars near the plane of a galaxy.
  Globular: a compact, spheroidal group of stars in the outskirts of galaxies.

Color-Brightness Diagram: a graph showing significant correlations between a star's spectral class and luminosity.

Constellation: a group of bright stars making a pattern in the sky, e.g., the Little Dipper or Southern Cross.

Copernican System: the theory which asserts that the earth rotates on its own axis and revolves around the sun.

Disk Star: a star located along the plane of the Milky Way.

Doppler Effect: the change in wave length observed when a body emitting light is moving toward (blue shift) or away (red shift) from an observer.

Ecliptic: the path of the sun among the stars.
  Plane of: the plane of the earth's orbit.

Escape Velocity: the speed which an object must attain to overcome the gravitational pull of a planet or other celestial body, and escape into space.

Galaxy: a large group of stars isolated in space from other such groups, and often containing gas and dust.

Giant: a star 15 to 40 times the diameter of the sun and approximately 100 times more luminous.

Halo: a spherical star cloud surrounding a galaxy.

Main-Sequence Star: one of a class of stars which show an orderly relationship between brightness, size and temperature.

Messier (M) Number: the designation of nebulae and star clusters in the Messier catalog.

Milky Way: the local galaxy, of which the sun is a member. Saucer-shaped, it looks like a river of stars in the sky because it is seen edge on from the earth.

Nebula: a hazy cloud of dust and gas outside the solar system. The term was formerly applied also to galaxies.

NGC Number: the designation of nebulae and star clusters in the *New General Catalogue*.

Nova: a star which becomes unstable, suddenly flaring up and then subsiding.

Perihelion: that point on a planet's orbit closest to the sun.

Ptolemaic System: a theory dominant until the 16th Century, asserting that the sun, moon, planets and stars all revolved around the earth.

Pulsating Star: one which periodically expands and then contracts. Includes Cepheids and RR Lyrae types.

Red Shift: *see Doppler Effect.*

Solar System: the sun and its planets, satellites, asteroids and comets.

Spectral Class: the classification of stars according to the principal features in their spectra.

Supergiant: a star approximately 50,000 times more brilliant than the sun and billions of miles in diameter.

Supernova: a very unstable star which suddenly explodes catastrophically.

Transit: the passage of a small celestial body across the face of a larger one.

Variable Star: one whose brightness varies periodically for reasons other than "twinkling" due to the earth's atmosphere.

White Dwarf: a planet-sized star with great density.

Zodiac: a band around the heavens centered on the ecliptic.

THE SOLAR SYSTEM

OBJECT	MILLION MILES FROM SUN	MEAN DIAMETER IN MILES	"YEAR"	"DAY"	KNOWN SATELLITES	ESCAPE VELOCITY MILES/SEC.	MASS (BILLION BILLION TONS)
Mercury	36	2,910	88 days	88 days	none	2.6	360
Venus	67	7,580	225 days	unknown	none	6.4	5,360
Earth	93	7,910	1 year	1 day	1	7.0	6,590
Mars	141	4,140	1.9 years	24.6 hours	2	3.1	705
Jupiter	483	86,600	11.9 years	10 hours	12	35.7	2,090,000
Saturn	888	72,300	29.7 years	10.5 hours	9	22.0	625,000
Uranus	1,780	29,500	83.7 years	10.7 hours	5	13.6	96,000
Neptune	2,800	27,800	166 years	12.7 hours	2	15.1	116,000
Pluto	3,660	3,700	247.7 years	6.4 days	unknown	unknown	unknown
Sun	———	865,000	———	25-33 days	———	383.	2,200,000,000
Moon	———	2,160	———	27.3 days	———	1.5	81

Bibliography

Solar System

Abetti, Giorgio, *The Sun*. Macmillan, 1957.

Baldwin, Ralph B., *The Face of the Moon*. University of Chicago Press, 1949.

Blanco, V. M., and S. W. Mc-Cuskey, *Basic Physics of the Solar System*. Addison-Wesley, 1961.

Fielder, Gilbert, *Structure of the Moon's Surface*. Pergamon Press, 1961.

Gamow, George, *The Moon*. Abelard-Schuman, 1959.

Kuiper, Gerard P., *Atmospheres of the Earth and Planets*. University of Chicago Press, 1952.

Kuiper, Gerard P., ed., *The Solar System* (Vols. I, II and III). University of Chicago Press, 1953, 1954, 1961.

Lalou, Étienne, *The Orion Book of the Sun*. Orion Press, 1960.

Menzel, Donald H., *Our Sun*. Harvard University Press, 1959.

Moore, Patrick, *A Guide to the Planets*. W. W. Norton, 1960. *The Planet Venus*. Macmillan, 1959.

*Nininger, Harvey H., *Out of the Sky*. University of Denver Press, 1952.

Nourse, Allan Edward, *Nine Planets*. Harper & Brothers, 1960.

Peek, Bertrand M., *The Planet Jupiter*. Macmillan, 1958.

Vaucouleurs, Gérard de, *The Planet Mars*. Macmillan, 1950.

*Watson, F. G., *Between the Planets*. Harvard University Press, 1956.

Whipple, F. L., *Earth, Moon and Planets*. Grosset & Dunlap, 1958.

Wilkins, Hugh, *Moon Maps*. Macmillan, 1960.

Wilkins, Hugh, and Patrick Moore, *The Moon*. Macmillan, 1955.

Stars and Stellar Systems

Bok, Bart J., and Priscilla F. Bok, *The Milky Way*. Harvard University Press, 1957.

*Couderc, Paul, *The Wider Universe*. Harper & Brothers, 1960.

†Hubble, Edwin P., *The Realm of the Nebulae*. Dover, 1958.

*Payne-Gaposchkin, Cecilia, *Stars in the Making*. Harvard University Press, 1952.

Sandage, Allan, *The Hubble Atlas of Galaxies*. Carnegie Institution of Washington, 1961.

Schwarzschild, Martin, *Structure and Evolution of the Stars*. Princeton University Press, 1958.

Shapley, Harlow, *Galaxies*. Harvard University Press, 1961.

Cosmology

*Barnett, Lincoln, *The Universe and Dr. Einstein*. William Sloane, 1957.

Bondi, H., W. B. Bonner, R. A. Lyttleton and G. J. Whitrow, *Rival Theories of Cosmology*. Oxford University Press, London, 1960.

*Bondi, H., *Cosmology*. Cambridge University Press, London, 1960.

†*The Universe at Large*. Doubleday, 1960.

*Eddington, Sir Arthur, *Space, Time and Gravitation*. Harper & Brothers, 1959. *The Expanding Universe*. Cambridge University Press, London, 1958.

*Gamow, George, *The Creation of the Universe*. Compass, 1960.

*Hoyle, Fred, *The Nature of the Universe*. Harper & Brothers, 1960.

Lyttleton, R. A., *Man's View of the Universe*. Little, Brown, 1961.

*Russell, Bertrand, *ABC of Relativity*. Oxford University Press, London, 1959.

*Sciama, D. W., *The Unity of the Universe*. Doubleday, 1959.

*Whitrow, G. J., *The Structure and Evolution of the Universe*. Hutchinson, London, 1959.

History

Abetti, Giorgio, *The History of Astronomy*. Abelard-Schuman, 1952.

*Bell, E. T., *Men of Mathematics*. Simon & Schuster, 1961.

†Berry, Arthur, *A Short History of Astronomy from the Earliest Times through the Nineteenth Century*. Dover, 1961.

Doig, Peter, *A Concise History of Astronomy*. Philosophical Library, 1951.

*Dreyer, John Louis, *A History of Astronomy from Thales to Kepler*. Dover, 1953.

King, H. C., *The History of the Telescope*. Sky Publishing, 1955.

Koestler, Arthur, *The Sleepwalkers*. Macmillan, 1959.

Pannekoek, A., *A History of Astronomy*. Interscience Publishers, 1961.

Ronan, Colin, *Changing Views of the Universe*. Macmillan, 1961.

Rousseau, Pierre, *Man's Conquest of the Stars*. W. W. Norton, 1961.

Sarton, George, *A History of Science* (Vols. I and II). Harvard University Press, 1952, 1959.

Singer, Charles, *A Short History of Scientific Ideas to 1900*. Oxford University Press, London, 1959.

Skywatching

Ball, Sir Robert S. (E. A. Beet, ed.), *Popular Guide to the Heavens*. George Philip & Son, London, 1955.

Branley, F. M., *Experiments in Skywatching*. Thomas Y. Crowell, 1959.

Ernst, B., and T. E. de Vries, *Atlas of the Universe*. Thomas Nelson & Sons, London, 1961.

Hood, P., *Observing the Heavens*. Oxford University Press, 1952.

Macpherson, Hector, *Guide to the Stars*. Philosophical Library, 1955.

Mayall, N., and M. Mayall, *Skyshooting; Hunting Stars with Your Camera*. The Ronald Press, 1949.

Mayall N., M. Mayall and J. Wyckoff, *The Sky Observer's Guide*. Golden Press, 1961.

Norton, Arthur P., and J. Gall Inglis, *Norton's Star Atlas and Reference Handbook*. Sky Publishing, 1959.

Sidgwick, J. B., *Amateur Astronomer's Handbook*. Macmillan, 1955.

*Zim, Herbert, and Robert H. Baker, *Stars*. Golden Press, 1956.

General

Baker, Robert H., *An Introduction to Astronomy*. Van Nostrand, 1961. *Astronomy*. Van Nostrand, 1959.

Beer, A., ed., *Vistas in Astronomy* (Vols. I, II, III, IV and V). Pergamon Press, 1955, 1956, 1960, 1962.

Duncan, John C., *Astronomy*. Harper & Brothers, 1955.

Hawkins, Gerald S., *Splendor in the Sky*. Harper & Brothers, 1961.

Howard, Neale, *Standard Handbook of Telescope Making*. Thomas Y. Crowell, 1959.

*Hoyle, Fred, *Frontiers of Astronomy*. Harper & Brothers, 1955.

Inglis, Stuart J., *Planets, Stars and Galaxies*. John Wiley & Sons, 1961.

*Jeans, Sir James, *The Universe around Us*. Cambridge University Press, London, 1953.

Lovell, A.C.B., *The Individual and the Universe*. Harper & Brothers, 1959.

McGraw-Hill Encyclopedia of Science and Technology. McGraw-Hill, 1960.

Miczaika, G. R., and William M. Sinton, *Tools of the Astronomer*. Harvard University Press, 1961.

Pecker, Jean-Claude, *The Orion Book of the Sky*. Orion Press, 1960.

Rudaux, Lucien, and Gérard de Vaucouleurs, *Larousse Encyclopédia of Astronomy*. Batchworth Press, Middlesex, Eng., 1959.

Seaborg, Glenn T., and Evans G. Valens, *Elements of the Universe*. E. P. Dutton, 1958.

*Shapley, Harlow, *Of Stars and Men*. Beacon Press, 1958.

Shapley, Harlow and H. E. Howarth, *Source Book in Astronomy*. Harvard University Press, 1956.

Shapley, Harlow, ed., *Source Book in Astronomy, 1900-1950*. Harvard University Press, 1960.

Skilling, W. T., and R. S. Richardson, *A Brief Text in Astronomy*. Henry Holt, 1959.

Sky and Telescope Magazine. Sky Publishing, Cambridge, Mass.

†Smith, Graham, *Radio Astronomy*. Penguin, 1960.

Struve, Otto, B. Lynds and H. Pillans, *Elementary Astronomy*. Henry Holt, 1959.

Van de Kamp, Peter, *Basic Astronomy*. Random House, 1952.

Wright, Helen, *Palomar*. Macmillan, 1952.

* Also available in paperback edition.

† Only available in paperback edition.

Index

Numerals in italics indicate a photograph or painting of the subject mentioned.

Index, *continued*

Picture Credits

Credits for pictures from left to right are separated by commas, top to bottom by dashes.

Cover: Mount Wilson and Palomar Observatories photo by William C. Miller; © 1959 California Institute of Technology. 8: Mount Wilson and Palomar Observatories. 10, 11: Matt Greene. 12: The Bettmann Archive. 13: Culver Pictures—Brown Brothers. 14: Matt Greene. 17: Courtesy *Bibliothèque Nationale*, Paris. 18: Courtesy Charles H. Smiley, Brown University. 19: Herbert Orth courtesy Metropolitan Museum of Art—courtesy Metropolitan Museum of Art. 20, 21: Courtesy Simone D. Gossner—The Smithsonian Institution. 22: Dmitri Kessel—Marc Riboud from Magnum. 23: Baldev. 24: Eric Schaal courtesy Metropolitan Museum of Art. 25: The Smithsonian Institution. 26, 27: N. R. Farbman courtesy University of California. 28: Erich Lessing from Magnum—The Smithsonian Institution. 29: Erich Lessing from Magnum. 30: University of Michigan. 32, 33: Culver Pictures. 34: Frank Vincent Vitullo. 35 through 39: Jim Egleson. 40: Gaetano Di Palma courtesy Radiophysics Laboratory CSIRO, Sydney, Australia. 41: Fritz Goro. 42, 43: Courtesy U.S. Navy—left courtesy The Science Museum, London; right Culver Pictures. 44: Margaret Bourke-White. 45, 46: J. R. Eyerman. 47: Mark A. Binn. 48, 49: Max Gschwind. 50: Mount Wilson and Palomar Observatories photo by William C. Miller; © 1959 California Institute of Technology—Warner and Swasey Observatory, Case Institute of Technology. 51: Warner and Swasey Observatory, Case Institute of Technology—Lick Observatory. 52, 53: Corning Glass Works, Peter Stackpole, Ralph Crane from Black Star. 54, 55: Ralph Crane from Black Star. 56, 57: Mount Wilson and Palomar Observatories except bottom left and bottom center J. R. Eyerman. 58: Larry Burrows. 59: Andreas Feininger. 60, 61: David Moore from Black Star except top left diagram by Mark A. Binn based on drawing by Max Gschwind for FORTUNE. 62: Chesley Bonestell from *Conquest of Space;* © 1944 reprinted by permission of the Viking Press, Inc. courtesy Willy Ley. 64: Matt Greene. 66 through 69: Gaetano Di Palma. 71: Russ Kinne from Photo Researchers. 72, 73: Mel Hunter. 74: Mel Hunter—Dr. Robert C. Leighton. 75: Chesley Bonestell—Dr. Robert C. Leighton. 76, 77: W. S. Finsen of Union Observatory, Johannesburg—Matt Greene. 78: Max Gschwind for FORTUNE—Fritz Goro. 79: E. C. Slipher, Lowell Observatory—E. C. Slipher and J. B. Edson, Lowell Observatory. 80: Nino Carbe, Australian News and Information Bureau. 81: Mount Wilson and Palomar Observatories. 82, 83: C. O. Lampland and E. C. Slipher, Lowell Observatory—Walter Curtin, United Press International, Lick Observatory. 84: Official U.S. Navy photo, Canton Island Expedition, 1937. 86, 87: Gaetano Di Palma. 91: Jim Egleson. 92: Frank Vincent Vitullo. 93: Gaetano Di Palma.

94: Frank Vincent Vitullo. 95: U.S. Air Force. 96, 97: Antonio Petruccelli. 98, 99: Mel Hunter. 100: J. R. Eyerman. 101: George Leavens—Ray Manley from Shostal. 102, 103: Left George Leavens courtesy High Altitude Observatory, Boulder, Colorado; right Sacramento Peak Observatory, U.S. Air Force Cambridge Research Laboratories—left Mount Wilson and Palomar Observatories; right High Altitude Observatory, Boulder, Colorado. 104, 105: Matt Greene. 106, 107: Lund Observatory. 108: Matt Greene. 109: Frank Vincent Vitullo. 110: Gaetano Di Palma. 112: Frank Vincent Vitullo. 115: Mount Wilson and Palomar Observatories. 116: Arthur D. Code and Theodore E. Houck of the University of Wisconsin—Mount Wilson and Palomar Observatories. 117: Max Gschwind for FORTUNE. 118, 119: George V. Kelvin. 120: George V. Kelvin—Mount Wilson and Palomar Observatories photo by William C. Miller; © 1959 California Institute of Technology. 121: George V. Kelvin—Official U.S. Navy photo by Arthur A. Hoag. 122, 123: Mount Wilson and Palomar Observatories photo by William C. Miller; © 1959 California Institute of Technology. 124: Alex Ebel. 125: Mel Hunter. 126, 127, 128: Mount Wilson and Palomar Observatories photo by William C. Miller; © 1959 California Institute of Technology. 132: Matt Greene. 137: Official U.S. Navy photo by Arthur A. Hoag. 138, 139, 140: Mount Wilson and Palomar Observatories photo by William C. Miller; © 1959 California Institute of Technology. 141: Mount Wilson and Palomar Observatories. 142: Lick Observatory photos by George Herbig. 143: Mount Wilson and Palomar Observatories. 144: J. R. Eyerman. 149: Gaetano Di Palma. 150, 151: Matt Greene. 155: Courtesy Columbia University. 156: Nino Carbe, Mount Wilson and Palomar Observatories. 157: Official U.S. Navy photo by Arthur A. Hoag. 158 through 161: Mount Wilson and Palomar Observatories photo by William C. Miller; © 1959 California Institute of Technology. 162, 163: Official U.S. Navy photo by Arthur A. Hoag. 164: Antonio Petruccelli. 165: Mount Wilson and Palomar Observatories. 166: J. R. Eyerman, News Bureau California Institute of Technology—Mount Wilson and Palomar Observatories, courtesy NBC "Wisdom" Television Series—J. R. Eyerman. 167: Henk Jonker—Bill Early, Mount Wilson and Palomar Observatories—News Bureau California Institute of Technology, Walter Daran. 168: Mount Wilson and Palomar Observatories. 170, 171: Frank Vincent Vitullo. 173: Matt Greene. 174, 175: Frank Vincent Vitullo. 177: Ralph Morse. 178: © Philippe Halsman. 179: Nino Carbe. 180: George V. Kelvin, Mount Wilson and Palomar Observatories. 181: George V. Kelvin. 182, 183: Matt Greene. 184: Harland Nasvik. 185: Mount Wilson and Palomar Observatories.

Acknowledgments

The editors of this book are particularly indebted to J. J. Nassau, Professor of Astronomy, Case Institute of Technology, and Simone Daro Gossner, who read the entire book and criticized the chapters in their own special areas. The editors are also indebted to Gerard P. Kuiper, Professor of Astronomy, University of Arizona; Allan R. Sandage, of the staff of Mount Wilson and Palomar Observatories; C. H. Stephenson, Assistant Professor of Astronomy, Case Institute of Technology; Charles A. Federer Jr., Editor, *Sky and Telescope* magazine; Charles H. Smiley, Director, Brown University Observatory; James R. Newman; Joseph Campbell; Derek Price, Department of Science and Technology, Yale University; James S. Pickering, Assistant Astronomer, Hayden Planetarium; Harry Bober, Associate Professor of Fine Arts, New York University; Llewellyn H. Thomas, Professor of Physics, Columbia University; and Harlow Shapley, Harvard University.

x

PRODUCTION STAFF FOR TIME INCORPORATED

Arthur R. Murphy Jr. (*Vice President and Director of Production*) Robert E. Foy, James P. Menton and Caroline Ferri

Text photocomposed on Photon equipment under the direction of Albert J. Dunn and Arthur J. Dunn

Printed by R. R. Donnelley & Sons Company, Crawfordsville, Indiana, and Livermore and Knight Co., Providence, Rhode Island

Paper by The Mead Corporation, Dayton, Ohio

Bound by R. R. Donnelley & Sons Company, Crawfordsville, Indiana